HOW ON
Terence McCarthy
earth?

Answers to the puzzles of our planet

SPONSOR'S FOREWORD

The African continent has a diverse and rich geological setting, representing the Earth's history since the beginning of time. Some of the old basement rocks of 3 800 million years, identified in South Africa, are remnants of the oldest continents.

Africa was part of a previous supercontinent, Gondwana, well known for its diverse flora and fauna. South Africa itself is blessed with two geological 'wonders of the world' – the Witwatersrand Goldfield and the Bushveld Igneous Complex. These two mega geological features of extreme geological interest and value have not been equalled anywhere in the world except perhaps for the oilfields of the Middle East.

Important for the human race is that discoveries until now indicate that Africa, and specifically South Africa, was probably the area where humans originated.

Since the late nineteenth century, mining as an industry has been crucial to South Africa, with precious metals and minerals contributing two-thirds of the country's mineral export earnings and over 30% of total goods exported. The mining industry is also South Africa's biggest employer, with around 460 000 employees and another 400 000 employed by suppliers of goods and services to the industry.

As a leading and diverse minerals resources group – with a portfolio spanning coal, mineral sands, base metals and iron ore – Exxaro takes its responsibility of preserving southern Africa's unique combination of mineral resources seriously through the sustainable extraction of ore and minerals. We are equally serious about our role in facilitating a better understanding of the Earth's geology and protecting the fragile environment in which we live.

It is our privilege to be associated with the respected group of contributors and editors responsible for the publication *How on Earth?*. We believe books of this nature play a vital role in educating the people of this planet about our collective past and the importance of ensuring our collective future.

Sipho Nkosi
Chief executive officer
Exxaro Resources Limited
www.exxaro.com

POWERING POSSIBILITY

Lanz von Hörsten / IOA

PREFACE

Perhaps the most important attributes that set humans apart from other animals are our ability to reason, to articulate our thoughts and to convey them to others. Humans are also naturally curious. Successive generations therefore did not have to rediscover knowledge, but learned from their elders who passed on the cumulative knowledge. One can imagine a scene, no doubt repeated in societies across the globe over many millennia, of a community sitting around a fire in the evening listening to the elders' discourse on the world, drawing on knowledge passed down over many generations. Perhaps the elders responded to questions from younger tribesmen and women, questions arising from their curiosity and from their wish to make sense of the world around them. Such traditions are still with us. The advent of writing and the spread of literacy have resulted in the replacement of the tribal elder by books and other media, but the urge to understand and make sense of the world is still very much alive. Even today, we all have questions about our world, and I think we all still secretly wish we had friendly elders we could ask. This book is very much a product of that tradition.

The rapid expansion of research in earth sciences and astronomy in the latter half of the twentieth century has brought about a radical transformation of our understanding of the Earth, how it works and how it has changed over the millennia. Although the questions posed in this book are focused primarily in the earth sciences, the answers are drawn from a wide range of disciplines, because such is the complex nature of the world. Every effort has been made to keep the answers short and concise and to strip away the mists of scientific jargon, making them accessible to all. Sources for further reading have been deliberately omitted, because although many excellent works exist, they are unlikely to be readily available in local libraries. My advice to readers seeking more information is to use the internet. Google and Google Scholar are especially useful.

The concept for this book was originally conceived by Nick Norman and Pippa Parker, and I was invited to turn it into reality. I thank Pippa and Nick for a great learning opportunity. Thanks also to: the editorial team of Leni Martin, Mike Lucas, Helen de Villiers and Colette Alves; Louise Topping for her excellent design; and Colin Bleach for his clear illustrations. I am grateful to my many colleagues who provided illustrations, and they are acknowledged in the book; to Maarten de Wit, Paul Skelton, Peter Ashton, Lucinda Backwell, Alex Kisters, Ludwig Combrink, Ray Durrheim, Ian Maclachlan, Greg Heath, John Drinkwater, Hans Smit, Melvyn Miles, Ursula Kibido, Matt Kitching and Bruce Rubidge for valuable discussions and help with acquiring illustrations; and Izak Rust who transformed the work into flowing Afrikaans. Thanks also to my wife Erna for support and encouragement.

Finally, I acknowledge the sponsorship provided by Exxaro, and thank Trevor Arran and Hilton Atkinson for their part in bringing this about. The sponsorship has made it possible to market the book at a reduced price and thus broaden the accessibility of the work.

Terence McCarthy

Terence McCarthy

CONTENTS

5 THE WORLD AROUND US 100

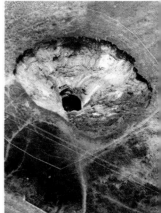

6 LIFE 144

GLOSSARY 168

INDEX 172

1 THE EARTH AND ITS ENVIRONMENT

WHAT IS THE SUN MADE OF?

Determining the composition of the Sun may seem like an impossible task. We obviously cannot get a sample of it to analyse in a laboratory, so how can we find out what it is made of? In fact, the task is relatively simple, and astronomers routinely determine the composition of stars, including the Sun. The method used relies on the spectral properties of elements and the nature of a star's outer atmosphere.

When a chemical element is heated, its atoms become excited and give off energy in the form of light. For example, if you throw a pinch of table salt (sodium chloride) into a fire, the flames turn bright yellow: when sodium atoms are heated they emit light of a specific wavelength that our eyes see as yellow. Other elements give off light of different wavelengths (or colours) when heated: calcium emits red light, for example, and copper, green. The characteristic light given off by a heated chemical element is known as its emission spectrum, which is determined using an instrument called a spectrograph.

The converse of this phenomenon is the absorption of light by an element's unexcited atoms. For example, if light consisting of the full wavelength spectrum (white light) passes through a cloud of unexcited atoms, they will absorb light spectra at their characteristic wavelengths, leaving dark gaps in the full light spectrum. This produces what is known as an absorption spectrum.

While the Sun's interior is hot and incandescent, emitting light of all wavelengths, its exterior is surrounded by a cooler atmosphere known as the photosphere. The outer reaches of the photosphere contain free, unexcited atoms, which absorb light emerging from the surface of the Sun, leaving dark lines in the solar spectrum known as Fraunhofer lines (so named in honour of Joseph von Fraunhofer, who first recognized their significance and produced a detailed map of the solar spectrum in 1815).

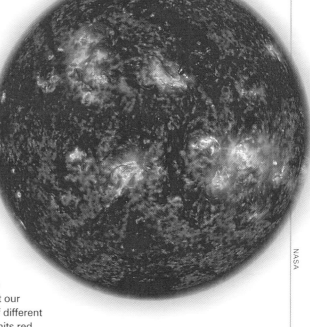

NASA

The Sun's surface is a churning mass of hot gases surrounded by a cooler atmosphere. Unlike Earth, the Sun's interior and atmosphere have the same composition.

By studying these dark lines, astronomers can determine the wavelengths absorbed and thus identify the elements responsible for the light absorption. Moreover, from the amount of light absorbed, the relative abundances of those elements in the solar atmosphere can be estimated. And because we believe the Sun to be fairly well mixed, the proportions of atoms in its outer atmosphere are assumed to be representative of the whole star. The same principles apply to any other star.

This spectral method works well for the more plentiful chemical elements in the Sun, but it is less accurate for rare

THE SOLAR ABSORPTION SPECTRUM

hydrogen   helium   hydrogen   helium

As sunlight passes through the solar atmosphere, atoms absorb certain wavelengths in the solar light spectrum, seen here as dark bands, which are used to identify which elements are present and their abundance.

'Starbursts' of coloured light from fireworks depend on the light emission spectra of the chemical elements added to the fireworks. Conversely, absorption of specific colours is used to determine the elemental composition of stars.

elements whose light absorption is much weaker. However, scientists can precisely determine the relative abundance of rare elements from carbonaceous chondrites, a type of meteorite believed to represent the less volatile materials from which the Sun and planets were formed (see page 12). Results gained from meteorite analyses agree closely with those from solar spectral measurements of the more abundant elements such as magnesium, and this provides confidence in the two approaches.

Just 10 elements make up 99.98% of the Sun's mass (weight). Hydrogen and helium are by far the most abundant, accounting for 98.1% of its mass. They are both normally gases, but the Sun's huge mass exerts a very strong gravitational field that squeezes the atoms closely together, making their consistency probably more like a liquid than a gas. The average density of the Sun is 1.4 g/cm^3 (the density of water is 1 g/cm^3), while the density of hydrogen at atmospheric pressure is 0.00009 g/cm^3 and helium about twice that.

THE 10 MOST ABUNDANT ELEMENTS IN THE SUN

ELEMENT	ABUNDANCE (% OF TOTAL MASS)
Hydrogen	71.0
Helium	27.1
Oxygen	0.97
Carbon	0.40
Iron	0.14
Silicon	0.099
Magnesium	0.076
Neon	0.058
Nitrogen	0.096
Sulphur	0.04

PORTION OF THE ABSORPTION SPECTRUM OF BETELGEUSE

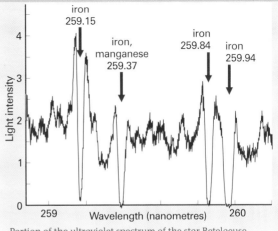

Portion of the ultraviolet spectrum of the star Betelgeuse showing absorption lines of iron and manganese.

WHAT MAKES THE SUN SHINE – AND HOW LONG WILL IT LAST?

Stars, such as our Sun, initially form in space by the accumulation of matter – gas and dust. As matter accumulates and the body grows, its gravity increases, attracting ever more matter, and resulting in ever greater gravity. Gravitational collapse heats the material and when the temperature reaches a certain point (in excess of 5 million°C) the process of nuclear fusion begins and a star is born. Nuclear fusion is the combining of atoms of one element to form a new element; in this case hydrogen atoms combine to form helium. Huge amounts of energy are released in the process so that the complete fusion of 1 kg of hydrogen, for example, produces 6.3×10^{14} joules of heat. To put this into perspective, fusing 1 g of hydrogen into helium produces the same amount of energy as would burning 500 tonnes of wood. Clearly, hydrogen fusion is a potent energy source – and it has been harnessed to make the hydrogen bomb. Indeed, the Sun and all similar young stars are, in effect, continuously exploding hydrogen bombs.

NUCLEAR FUSION – SOURCE OF THE SUN'S ENERGY

The Sun and similar stars derive their energy by converting hydrogen into helium. In this process, four atoms of hydrogen fuse (or combine) to form one atom of helium. The process occurs in three steps: first, two protons (hydrogen nuclei) fuse and a positron (a positively charged electron) is expelled, resulting in a nucleus consisting of one proton and one neutron (known as deuterium or hydrogen 2). Next, the deuterium combines with a further proton to produce a nucleus containing two protons and one neutron (helium 3). Finally, two helium 3 nuclei fuse to produce a helium 4 nucleus (two protons and two neutrons) and two separate protons (hydrogen nuclei).

hydrogen · deuterium · helium 3 · hydrogen · hydrogen · hydrogen · hydrogen · [H] · deuterium [2H] · helium 3 [3He] · hydrogen · helium 4 [4He] · hydrogen · E

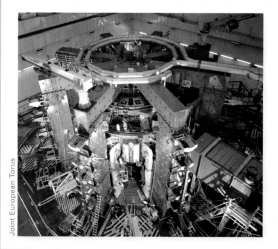

Joint European Torus

Physicists continue to seek ways to make hydrogen fusion reactions occur under controlled conditions so that some of the Earth's abundant hydrogen can be used to produce a limitless supply of pollution-free energy. Mass for mass, the fusion process generates far more energy than the fission or splitting of atoms of uranium, which is the process used in nuclear power plants today to create energy.

Physicists are striving to harness the immense power of nuclear fusion to provide an unlimited, pollution-free energy source for humanity. The main difficulty is to contain the atoms, which only react at extremely high temperatures. The tokamak, pictured here, is a device that could do this by confining the reacting atoms using magnetic fields.

US Department of Energy / Science Photo Library

Like the Sun, the hydrogen bomb derives its energy from the fusion of atoms of hydrogen.

Hydrogen fusion in the Sun is a self-regulating process that works through the interplay between the energy-generating nuclear reactions and the force of the Sun's gravity. If too much energy is produced, the Sun expands slightly and cools, slowing the reactions. If the reactions become too slow, energy production declines and gravity causes the Sun to contract, raising the temperature again and thus increasing the energy output. In this way, balance is maintained and there is no possibility of a runaway reaction. However, the Sun has been consuming hydrogen – and producing helium – for about 4 500 million years and its temperature has been slowly rising as helium has accumulated. It is believed that the Sun is now about 30% hotter than it was when hydrogen fusion began.

How long will our Sun's energy last? Scientists estimate that the Sun originally had enough hydrogen to last for about 10 000 million years. In these terms it is middle aged, with 5 000 million years or so to go. Ironically, had the Sun been bigger it would have had a shorter life, because larger stars consume their fuel faster than smaller ones. When excessive amounts of helium accumulate in a star, the energy output in its deep interior declines and gravity crushes the core, raising its temperature. At about 100 million°C, helium begins to fuse to make heavier elements and a series of processes are initiated that continue to produce energy, but which ultimately result in the death of the star. Conversely, if the star is too small, it will slowly fizzle out because there is insufficient mass to drive the fusion process to its natural limit. Fortunately, our Sun is just larger than this category. In contrast, stars larger than the Sun eventually disintegrate at the end of their lives in spectacular explosions known as supernovae.

The death of a star is an all-embracing astronomical event. When helium fusion begins, the intense heat causes the star's outer layers to expand and cool, so the star becomes red rather than the brilliant blue of the hydrogen-fusing period. Such stars are known as Red Giants and many – such as Betelgeuse in the constellation of Orion – are visible in the night sky. When our Sun finally enters this phase of its life, it will expand and envelop the Earth, evaporating the oceans and incinerating all life. Finally, friction from the solar atmosphere will slow the Earth in its orbit and cause it to plunge down into the Sun's core. However, there is no need to have sleepless nights about this fiery fate that awaits our beloved Earth – it's not going to happen for another 5 000 million years!

WHEN AND HOW DID THE EARTH FORM?

Our Solar System lies in the Milky Way galaxy, which looks similar to the Whirlpool galaxy shown in this Hubble Telescope image.

NASA

Earth is part of the Solar System, so to discover its origin, we must examine the Solar System as a whole. At its centre is the Sun, surrounded by eight major and several minor planets, as well as numerous smaller bodies that include asteroids in its inner regions and Pluto-like objects on the outer fringes. All these objects vary in composition. The inner planets of Mercury, Venus, Earth, Mars and the asteroids consist of dense, rocky material (silicate) and have metallic cores of iron and nickel, whereas the outer planets of Jupiter, Saturn, Uranus, Neptune and the Pluto-like objects consist mainly of frozen gases (hydrogen, helium, ammonia, oxides of carbon and methane) and water around small rocky cores. They all orbit the Sun in the same direction and lie more or less in the same plane, suggesting that they all formed similarly, despite their differing compositions.

The Solar System is part of the Milky Way galaxy, a vast disc consisting of billions of stars and massive clouds of gas and dust, all arranged in spiral structures or 'arms'. The clouds consist of material left over from the formation of the universe and debris from stars that ended their lives in cataclysmic explosions, or supernovae. Our Solar System began when part of one of these gas and dust clouds became compressed by a nearby supernova, creating a region of slightly higher density.

The denser compressed region, called the Solar Nebula, began to collapse under the force of its own gravity and as material streamed towards its centre, particles collided and caused the inner part to heat up from a very chilly -270 °C. With rising temperature, solid particles began to vaporize, continuing until all material near the centre had turned into gas. Due to an initial slight rotation, the cloud began to spin faster and faster as it collapsed, flattening into a disc shape, and material at its centre became hotter and denser. Electrons were stripped from atoms and their bare nuclei

were squeezed together, ultimately initiating nuclear fusion and the Sun's birth (see page 8).

Near the Sun, all material existed as vapour. Further out, only compounds with exceptionally high boiling points formed solid particles, such as compounds of silica, magnesium and iron, and a metallic iron–nickel alloy. Even further out, materials with a lower boiling point also formed solid particles, while in the cloud's outermost reaches, ice, solid methane, carbon monoxide, carbon dioxide and ammonia were probably present.

These particles began to clump together as planetesimals that grew to kilometres in diameter, which in turn amalgamated as planets. Mercury, Venus, Earth and Mars formed in the hot inner portion of the Solar Nebula and are composed mostly of iron–magnesium silicates with iron–nickel cores. Once started, the process seems to have been relatively rapid, taking perhaps a few tens of millions of years only. It was also extremely violent, with planetesimals raining down on the growing Earth. One collision was so violent that it vaporized part of Earth, producing the Moon (see page 20). Finally, about 3 900 million years ago, several large bodies struck Earth in a period known as the Late Bombardment. This may have been triggered by shifts in the orbits of Jupiter and Saturn, which sent planetesimals from more distant reaches of the Solar System into the inner region. Victims of the celestial violence are asteroids and planetesimal debris that orbit between Mars and Jupiter, which represent an unformed planet because of gravitational disruption by Jupiter.

The Eagle Nebula is a vast cloud of gas and dust in which stars, and possibly solar systems, are forming. Radiation from a star (top right, out of view) has shaped the dust into spectacular columns millions of kilometres tall.

NASA

Unlike the rocky inner planets and asteroids, the outer planets of Jupiter and beyond are composed mainly of gaseous materials and volatile compounds that were solidified by intense pressure and extreme cold. Volatile materials are far more abundant in cosmic dust than silicate material (see page 8), so the outer planets are generally much larger, but nonetheless formed in a similar way to the inner planets.

Not all the gas and dust in the Solar Nebula collapsed to form planets. Once nuclear fusion commenced in the Sun, it began to eject a stream of high-energy particles, called the Solar Wind, which swept away gas and dust not yet accreted into planetary bodies.

The Solar System is 4 567 million years old, as revealed by radiometric dating (see page 24) of material from meteorites that formed in the hot, inner Solar Nebula. Earth cannot be dated in this way because it is geologically very active and no longer has rocks that survive from its formation. However, the Earth would have formed a little later, but probably over 30 to 40 millions of years. After growing to about 60% of its present size, the Moon was formed from debris split from Earth by a planetesimal impact 4 530 million years ago (see page 20). The oldest terrestrial material found so far is a 4 404 million-year-old grain of zircon (see page 24), which indicates that Earth by then had a solid and geologically active crust. Earth's age must therefore lie between 4 567 and 4 404 million years old, with a best estimate of about 4 540 million years.

FORMATION OF THE SOLAR SYSTEM

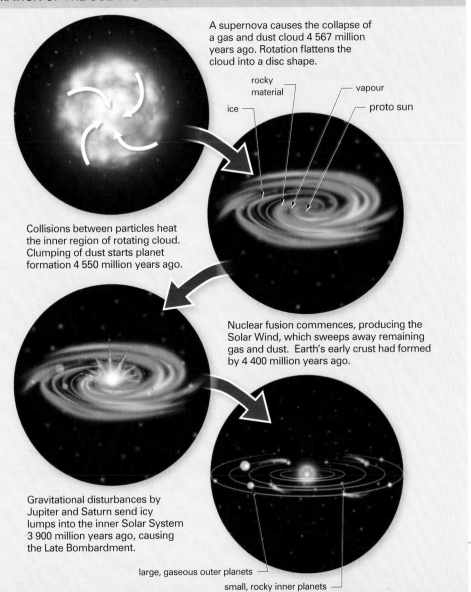

A supernova causes the collapse of a gas and dust cloud 4 567 million years ago. Rotation flattens the cloud into a disc shape.

rocky material

ice

vapour

proto sun

Collisions between particles heat the inner region of rotating cloud. Clumping of dust starts planet formation 4 550 million years ago.

Nuclear fusion commences, producing the Solar Wind, which sweeps away remaining gas and dust. Earth's early crust had formed by 4 400 million years ago.

Gravitational disturbances by Jupiter and Saturn send icy lumps into the inner Solar System 3 900 million years ago, causing the Late Bombardment.

large, gaseous outer planets

small, rocky inner planets

WHERE DOES EARTH'S WATER COME FROM?

Science Institute) and National Optical Astronomy Observatory/Association of Universities for Research in Astronomy/National Science Foundation

The Earth formed in the hot, inner region of the Solar System and probably remained largely molten during its growth. Water, nitrogen and carbon dioxide, which gave rise to the early oceans and atmosphere, were probably delivered towards the end of the accretion period by comets, which consist mostly of water ice and frozen carbon dioxide.

The existence of water and gases such as nitrogen and carbon dioxide on the planets closest to the Sun (Venus, Earth, Mars) – and on Earth in particular, which is a singularly watery planet – is something of an enigma because these substances have low boiling points and would have been present only as vapour in the inner region of the Solar System where these planets formed (see page 12). Consequently, the inner planets should have very low amounts of these substances.

An explanation for this favoured by some scientists is that minerals containing chemically combined water, nitrogen and carbon dioxide were present in the dust cloud from

Surface features on Mars such as this river delta indicate that it once hosted large rivers and oceans and probably would have been similar in appearance to Earth – a blue planet.

NASA

which the planets formed. After the Earth was formed, the subsequent decomposition and release of the compound constituents created the Earth's oceans and atmosphere. However, such compounds mostly decompose at relatively low temperatures, so the Earth and the other inner planets would have to have formed under low temperature conditions, which seems unlikely.

Instead, as described on page 12, it is more likely that the Earth formed in the hot interior of a cosmic dust cloud from iron-magnesium-silicate compounds that contained no water or carbon dioxide. Earth grew in size as clumps of dust (planetesimals) rained down on it, and it remained largely in a molten state due to the prevailing high temperature and the heat generated by the impacts of planetesimals. Earth began to cool and solidify only when this bombardment abated.

Meanwhile, the Solar Wind was blowing away from the Sun and sweeping vaporized water and carbon dioxide out of the inner region of the Solar System. In the early stages of its development, therefore, the Earth probably had no water at all. So where did its water and atmosphere come from?

It seems likely that the Earth only later acquired water and atmospheric gases, especially carbon dioxide, after its surface had cooled and solidified. The most probable sources were carbon-rich planetesimals and comets, the latter consisting of a mixture of water ice and frozen carbon dioxide. These substances originated in the outer region of the Solar System and beyond, where the temperature was low enough during planetary formation to allow carbon dioxide to freeze, so that Earth's early atmosphere consisted mostly of carbon dioxide imported from afar (see page 54).

But why should these bodies migrate to the inner reaches of the Solar System? They were apparently deflected by the gravitational fields of the large outer planets, especially Jupiter and Saturn, whose orbits underwent substantial changes during the first few hundred million years after planetary formation. The changes culminated in the Late Bombardment, which took place about 3 900 million years ago and resulted in the inner planets and their moons being struck by numerous large bodies. The large, roughly circular dark patches on the face of the Moon were formed in this way. It is likely that these, and earlier collisions, delivered the necessary ingredients to Earth for the oceans and atmosphere to form. Such extraterrestrial imports are by no means over, as comets from the outermost regions of the Solar System still occasionally enter Earth's neighbourhood.

In the early Solar System, Venus, Earth and Mars probably all had oceans and atmospheres of carbon dioxide with some nitrogen. Venus became overwhelmed by a runaway greenhouse effect, which vaporized its oceans. Mars lost its water by photo-oxidation, and its atmosphere too, because Martian gravity was too weak. It also lost its magnetic field. Uniquely, life on Earth transformed its atmosphere and regulated its temperature, so keeping its oceans.

NASA

Venus

Earth

Mars

Not to scale

HOW WAS THE EARTH FIRST WEIGHED?

Before discussing this question, we need to resolve some terminology. First, the weight of an object is really the force with which it is attracted to the Earth by gravity. Secondly, the amount of material making up an object is called its mass. For example, the mass of the Apollo astronauts was the same on Earth as on the Moon, but their weight on the Moon was about one sixth because of its weaker gravitational attraction. An astronaut will experience weightlessness (zero weight) when in orbit, but his or her mass will remain unchanged. Hence, when we talk of Earth's weight, we really mean its mass.

A way of measuring the Earth's mass was formulated by Sir Isaac Newton in 1666, based on his discovery of the mathematical laws that describe gravity. Legend has it that Newton was relaxing in the shade beneath an apple tree when an apple fell on him. This got him thinking – why do objects fall to Earth? He reasoned that there must be a force of attraction between them. Newton realized that this force – gravity – must be a fundamental property of all matter, including Earth. He went on to work out that the force of attraction between any two bodies depends on their masses and the square of the distance between them. Written mathematically, this is:

$$F = \frac{G \times M_1 \times M_2}{r^2}$$

where G is the Gravitational Constant, M_1 and M_2 are the masses of the two bodies and r is the distance between their centres. This mathematical expression of the Universal Law of Gravitation provided a means for determining Earth's mass.

The force, F, with which a mass M_1 is attracted to Earth is easily measured. Hence, the mass of the Earth, M_2, can be calculated provided r and G are known. The term r is simply the radius of the Earth, which was known, so only the value of G was needed to calculate the mass of the Earth. Nevil Maskelyne, the British Astronomer Royal, attempted to determine G in the mid 1700s by measuring the sideways deflection of a pendulum of known mass caused by a mountain. The distance from the centre of mass of the mountain to the pendulum and the mass of the mountain had to be estimated, so needless to say, the results were not very accurate. Instead, Henry Cavendish, a wealthy recluse with a deep interest in

APPARATUS USED TO WEIGH THE EARTH

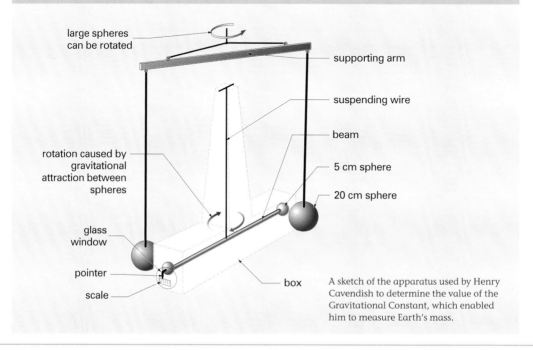

large spheres can be rotated

supporting arm

suspending wire

beam

rotation caused by gravitational attraction between spheres

5 cm sphere

20 cm sphere

glass window

pointer

scale

box

A sketch of the apparatus used by Henry Cavendish to determine the value of the Gravitational Constant, which enabled him to measure Earth's mass.

chemistry and physics, measured the value of **G** under controlled laboratory conditions. He achieved this in 1798, using apparatus built some years earlier by the Rev John Mitchell, who unfortunately died before he himself could obtain any results. The apparatus consisted of a 100 cm long wire secured at one end, which supported a horizontal beam. Attached to each end of the beam were lead spheres about 5 cm in diameter. Suspended by the wire, the beam was perfectly balanced, and was encased in a box to isolate it from air movements. A similar arrangement was constructed outside the box. Two lead spheres about 20 cm in diameter were suspended from an arm in such a way that they could be brought into close proximity to the spheres inside the box by rotating the supporting arm. Gravitational attraction between the spheres would cause the beam inside the box to rotate, creating a twisting force in the wire, which opposed the attraction between the spheres. A window in the side of the box permitted Cavendish to see and measure how much the beam was deflected. The entire apparatus was placed in a sealed room to keep the temperature uniform and Cavendish made the measurements from outside the room using a telescope, so that his own mass and body heat would not affect the measurements.

Astronauts such as Mark Shuttleworth (above), experience weightlessness when in orbit. On the Moon (below) astronauts weigh about a sixth of their normal weight because of the Moon's weak gravitational attraction.

Cavendish determined the twisting strength of the wire by measuring the period of oscillation of the beam. Using the wire's twisting strength and the measured deflection of the beam, he was able to calculate the force of attraction between the spheres, which is the term **F** in the Universal Law of Gravitation equation. M_1 and M_2 were the known masses of the spheres, and **r** was the distance between the spheres. As **G** was then the only unknown remaining, he could thus calculate its value. Once **G** was known, he was able to calculate the Earth's mass.

This turned out to be 6×10^{24} kg, or if written in full, 6 followed by 24 zeros. This very large number is rather meaningless to us. Cavendish was actually more interested in calculating the density of the Earth (mass/volume), which he determined to be 5.48 g/cm³. This is close to the value generally accepted today (5.519 g/cm³). As common rocks have a density of about 2.9 g/cm³, Earth's higher density indicates the presence of a dense core.

Once the mass of the Earth and **G** were known, it became possible to measure the masses and densities of the Sun and all the other planets, again using Newton's Universal Law of Gravitation. For example, the density of Jupiter is 1.34 g/cm³, so it clearly differs in composition from Earth.

WHY IS THE CENTRE OF THE EARTH HOT?

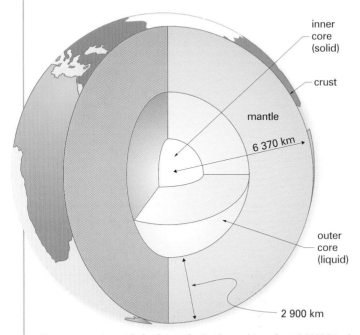

Temperature rises with depth into the Earth, reaching about 5 500°C in the inner core. Despite this, most of Earth's interior is solid, because the melting temperature of minerals rises with increasing pressure. Only the outer layer of the Earth's core is molten.

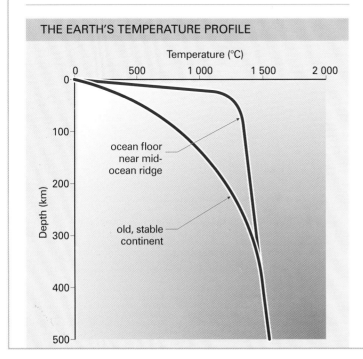

THE EARTH'S TEMPERATURE PROFILE

As workers in South Africa's gold and platinum mines know, the temperature underground increases the deeper they go. For example, in South Africa's deep-level gold mines, rock temperature increases by about 12°C per km depth. With the deepest mines now approaching a depth of 4 km, rock temperature at the bottom of such mines is typically 60–65°C. Temperature gradients in the Earth are very variable, ranging from about 5°C per km in recent thick sedimentary deposits to roughly 75°C per km in volcanically active areas. However, these gradients taper off as the depth increases, and below about 300 km the increase in temperature evens out to about 0.5°C per km.

At Earth's centre, the temperature is about 5 500°C. Even at such a very high temperature, the rocks are actually solid although slightly plastic (like warm toffee) because, as pressure increases towards the Earth's core, so too does the melting temperature. Only the outer portion of the Earth's core is molten; it is fortunate that this molten layer exists, because convection currents in the molten material give rise to the Earth's magnetic field, which forms a crucial protective shield around our planet. The energy required to drive convection in the outer core probably comes from latent heat release as the liquid outer core solidifies at the boundary with the solid inner core.

So why is the Earth so hot inside? Firstly, it formed under extremely hot conditions in the inner reaches of the Solar System (see page 12).

(see page 12)

Temperature increases with depth, but the rate at which this happens is regionally variable, as shown here. Below about 300 km, however, temperature becomes more uniform, and increases slowly with depth.

In addition, it grew in size as planetesimals collided and amalgamated with it, increasing its temperature to above its melting point in the early stages of its development. When this accretion process tailed off, heat would have been rapidly lost into space by radiation and a solid crust would have formed on the planet's molten outer skin.

From then on, the rate of cooling would have been moderated by the crust's relative inability to conduct heat, because rocks are poor and slow heat conductors. Below the crust, the slightly plastic but still solid rocks of the mantle undergo slow convection, thereby increasing the rate of heat loss and cooling. Hot, plastic rock rises in the Earth, displacing cooler rock, which sinks. In this way, heat is physically carried outwards, but at a rate faster than it can be transferred and lost by conduction through the rocky outer crust. Using this information, the nineteenth-century physicist, Lord Kelvin, calculated that the Earth was between 20 and 40 million years old, based on the time required for a molten Earth to cool to its present-day temperature. He argued, wrongly as it turns out, that the Earth would be cold inside if it were much older than this.

Our understanding of the Earth's heat budget was radically changed by the discovery of radioactivity by Henri Becquerel in 1896 and, in 1903, by Marie Curie's realization that radioactive decay produces heat. There are three important radioactive elements in the Earth; the isotopes of uranium and thorium and one of the isotopes of potassium (^{40}K). We do not know their exact concentrations in the deep Earth, so we cannot be sure of the amount of heat they produce. However, if we assume that they are as abundant as in the most common chondrite meteorites (which are believed to represent the material from which Earth formed – see page 8), the calculated heat production is very similar to the estimated heat loss from the Earth (0.2 W/m^2). This suggests that most heat produced by the Earth is probably derived from internal radioactive decay, with the remainder being primordial heat acquired during the planet's formation.

Is the centre of the Earth getting cooler? Although uncertainties abound, particularly with regard to the concentrations of Earth's radioactive elements and the rate of heat loss, there is no doubt that the Earth is cooling. It is doing so, however, at an extremely slow rate because the half-lives of the three radioactive elements concerned are thousands of millions of years. Nevertheless, heat loss from the interior is undoubtedly the most fundamentally important process taking place on Earth, because it ultimately drives most of the geological activity on the planet. Once it has cooled and geological activity ceases, the Earth will no longer be able to support anything but the simplest forms of life, and possibly not even those.

Grant Cawthorn

In areas of current or recent volcanic activity, geothermal gradients are very high and hot springs abound. In Iceland, such hot springs generate sufficient electricity to power the entire island.

HOW DID THE MOON FORM?

Earth and the other planets formed when grains of solid material orbiting the nascent Sun began to clump together due to mutual gravitational attraction about 4 570 million years ago (see page 12). By about 4 530 million years ago, Earth had grown to about 65% of its present size and the segregation of its iron-nickel core was well advanced.

At this time, Earth collided with a body about the size of Mars (diameter 6 787 km), which may have been a second planet growing in the same orbital region as Earth. The impact was so violent that it vaporized both the impacting body and a large part of Earth's mantle. This vapour began to orbit the young Earth and condensed into solid particles, some of which coalesced to form the embryonic Moon. Thereafter, both the Moon and Earth continued to grow by amalgamating more incoming material. The intense heat generated by these collisions melted the growing Moon, and its initial anorthosite crust formed – about 4 500 million years ago. (It is likely that Earth once had a similar anorthosite crust, but geological recycling has removed all trace of it.) As a consequence of this history, the Moon's core is relatively smaller than Earth's, but its mantle and basaltic crust are basically similar.

NASA

The lunar surface consists of light-coloured, heavily cratered Lunar Highlands that represent its ancient, original crust, and the dark, sparsely cratered Lunar Mare.

COMPARISON OF THE INTERIORS OF THE EARTH AND MOON

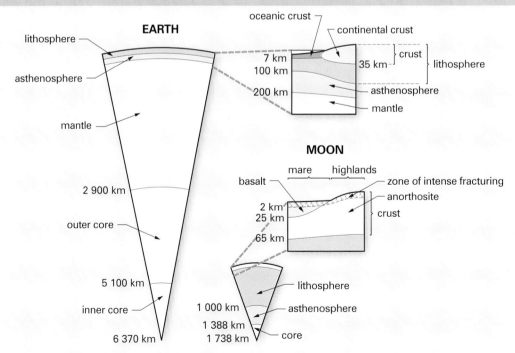

The structure of the Earth and Moon is quite different. The Moon's core is small, continental crust is absent, and its outer skin consists of fragmental material produced by 4 billion years of cosmic bombardment.

The effects of the incessant rain of rocky particles onto the Moon's surface during its final growth phase are preserved in the older Highland areas, where the pale-coloured, rocky crust is extensively cratered. The grand finale occurred about 3 900 million years ago when, in a period known as the Late Bombardment, several massive bodies collided with the Moon, forming huge circular lunar 'seas', or 'maria' on the surface. Voluminous basalt lavas subsequently erupted and filled the craters left by these impacts. After this, geological activity on the Moon effectively ceased.

Like all the inner planets, the Moon is composed of rocky material, but it differs from Earth in important ways. For example, the Moon's density is just 3.34 g/cm³ compared to Earth's density of 5.5 g/cm³ because it has a proportionately smaller core. Rocks on the Moon's surface are very old, ranging in age from 4 500 million to about 3 100 million years, as revealed by samples brought back by the Apollo and Luna missions. In contrast, rocks on Earth older than 3 000 million years are very rare because of later geological reworking. The absence of young rocks on the Moon indicates that significant geological activity ceased there long ago. Its surface is therefore like a time capsule, providing insight into the earliest period of its own history, as well as that of Earth.

Many of the planets orbiting the Sun have moons but, in general, these moons are tiny compared to their host planets. Our Moon is an exception, having a diameter of 3 476 km that is only slightly smaller than the diameter of Mercury (4 880 km) and just over a quarter of the diameter of Earth (12 756 km). In fact, the Moon is so large in relation to Earth that the Earth-Moon pair can be regarded as a double planet system, like Pluto and its large moon, Charon.

We commonly think of the Moon as revolving around Earth, but in reality the Earth and Moon rotate around a common centre of gravity, like a pair of ice skaters spinning together while holding hands. This association has exerted a powerful stabilizing influence on the orientation of Earth's axis of rotation and may even have contributed significantly to making our planet habitable. It has

NASA

Apollo astronauts brought back samples of lunar rocks to help scientists decipher the Moon's history.

been calculated that, in the absence of the Moon, the tilt in the Earth's axis, which currently lies at an angle of 23.5° relative to the plane of its orbit, would be highly unstable and would vary from 0° to about 85° in a completely random manner over tens of millions of years. At a tilt of 85°, half of the Earth would be light for nearly six months, and the other half in darkness. The dark side would undoubtedly freeze over. At a tilt of 0° the day length would be the same virtually everywhere (except near the poles) and there would be no seasons. Moreover, ocean tidal range would be very small. Under these conditions, life cycles of organisms would be subject to continual and random disruption, and it is unlikely that advanced forms or perhaps any form of life could have evolved on Earth.

University of Cape Town Libraries

In 1971, a group of South African scientists from the University of Cape Town participated in the study of lunar samples returned by the Apollo astronauts. The team was: standing (left to right): Mike Orren, Pierre Hofmeyr and Terence McCarthy; (seated, left to right): James Willis, Prof Louis Ahrens (Principal Investigator) and Tony Erlank. Inset: John Gurney.

HOW STABLE IS THE EARTH'S MAGNETIC FIELD?

A compass works because the Earth behaves as if it had a giant bar magnet inside it that is aligned, more or less, along its axis of rotation. A compass needle is itself a magnet and it aligns itself in the Earth's magnetic field. The Earth's field is very weak – much weaker than a fridge magnet – but it is very important and the Earth would have been a very different place if it did not have the protection provided by its magnetic field.

The supposed internal magnet is not aligned exactly along the Earth's axis of rotation, so the compass needle points to magnetic north rather than true north; the angle between the two is known as the magnetic declination, which varies from place to place and also over time. Moreover, at different latitudes a compass needle tends to point into the Earth to varying degrees. At the equator it rests horizontally, whereas at the magnetic poles it points vertically downwards. This is called magnetic inclination.

The Earth may behave as if it has a giant magnet inside it, but we know that this is not actually the case. Natural magnets lose their magnetism at a certain temperature known as the Curie point, which is about 770°C for iron. It is estimated that the temperature in the centre of the Earth's iron-nickel core is in the region of 5 500°C, well above the Curie point, so there is clearly no magnet in the Earth. Scientists believe that the field is formed electromagnetically by means of a complex process involving thermal circulation in the molten outer regions of the metallic core, the rotation of the Earth and possibly the Sun's magnetic field. It appears that the core hosts not one but many separate magnets (called magnetic domains) that combine to form the Earth's total field. These domains slowly shift position, causing the magnetic poles to move, thereby changing the magnetic declination.

It is possible to gather information about the Earth's magnetic field in the past because when rocks form they record the orientation of the field. For example, during the formation of mudstone by the slow settling of sediment particles in water, any grains of the magnetic mineral magnetite present will align themselves parallel with the Earth's magnetic field and become compacted into the resulting rock. The rock will thus become a weak magnet, like a compass aligned in the Earth's field. As long as it is not subsequently heated above its Curie point (about 580°C for magnetite), it will retain the orientation of the magnetic field, even if the rock's position is subsequently changed, say by folding of sedimentary layers. Igneous rocks can also acquire a natural magnetism. As grains of magnetite in these rocks cool through the Curie point, they take on a magnetic field aligned with that of the Earth.

This magnetic field preserved in rocks is called palaeomagnetism. Using very sensitive equipment, we can measure the orientation of the field and discover not only the north direction, but also the latitude at which the rock formed, as determined from its magnetic inclination. During the 1950s, when the study of palaeomagnetism was still in its infancy, routine measurements of the orientation of the magnetic field preserved in relatively young igneous

THE EARTH'S MAGNETIC FIELD

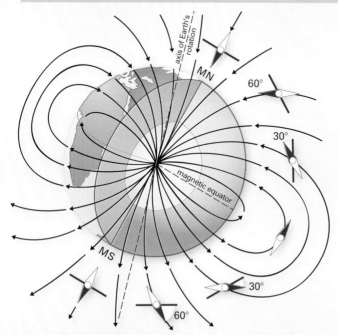

The Earth behaves like a large magnet that aligns compass needles horizontally at the Equator, but dips them towards the poles at an angle that varies with latitude.

THE RECORD OF MAGNETIC FIELD REVERSALS

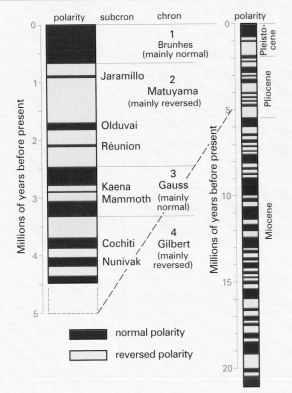

polarity	subcron	chron	polarity

The Earth's magnetic field has frequently reversed over the past 250 million years, most recently just 780 000 years ago. Signs suggest it may soon reverse again.

beneath southern Africa has already reversed its polarity. Compasses in the region still point north, however, because the global field continues to dominate. The rate of movement of the magnetic poles has also increased dramatically in recent decades. It is therefore surmised that a polar reversal may be commencing. The last polar reversal took place about 780 000 years ago.

The Earth's magnetic field is important because it shields the Earth from the impact of the Solar Wind – a stream of charged particles (mainly electrons and protons) ejected at high velocities by the Sun. The magnetic field largely deflects these particles away from the Earth, thus preventing them from interacting with the atmosphere. Without a magnetic field, it is probable that the Solar Wind would have stripped away the Earth's atmosphere. The magnetic field also keeps the Solar Wind well away from our sensitive communication satellites, protects our extensive power grids from the ravages of most Solar storms and ensures that radiation levels at the cruising altitudes of jet liners is low. There are also indications that loss of the magnetic field might result in loss of the ozone layer, causing a massive increase in the intensity of ultraviolet radiation at the Earth's surface.

rocks led to the surprising discovery that the Earth's magnetic field had periodically reversed, with the north and south magnetic poles switching places. Time spans when the field was aligned as it is at present became known as 'normal polarity periods', and the opposite alignment 'reversed polarity periods'. The record of magnetic reversals has been studied in great detail and is well known for as far back as about 250 million years.

We do not know the cause of magnetic reversal, and are uncertain about the process by which the field changes. What seems to happen is that magnetic domains in the core change polarity individually. This results in a weakening of the overall field until it disappears completely. It then gradually reforms and strengthens as more domains assume the new polarity direction.

The Earth's magnetic field is weakening at an alarming rate, particularly over southern Africa. At the Hermanus Magnetic Observatory, the field has weakened by about 20% since measurements began in 1940, and it is believed that a magnetic domain

The National Research Foundation has its principal magnetic observatory at Hermanus in the Western Cape. Sensitive magnetometers record movement of the magnetic poles and the magnetic field's strength.

HOW ARE ROCKS DATED?

Dating rocks has enabled scientists to unravel the complex histories of the Earth and Moon. From the eighteenth century, scientists in Europe began to map the relative age and distribution of layered sedimentary rocks, based on the fact that younger layers are deposited on top of older ones. They could also establish the relative ages of sedimentary rocks based on fossils preserved in the rock layers, including those from different continents. Even igneous rocks could sometimes be dated from their relationship to fossil-bearing rocks. In this way, a relative chronology was established for most rock formations in Europe. But despite this, the many igneous and sedimentary rocks without fossils could not be dated. The absolute age of different rocks also remained controversial. Geologists claimed that the oldest rocks were hundreds of millions of years old, while physicists put them at tens of millions of years old, but to creationist theologians, they could be no more than mere thousands of years old.

The discovery of radioactivity in 1896 provided a means to settle the debate. Radioactivity results from the ejection of particles from the atomic nucleus of a (parent) chemical element, causing it to change into another (daughter) element over a period of time. According to the law of radioactivity (formulated by Ernest Rutherford and Frederick Soddy in 1902), the more radioactive atoms there are, the more will decay in a given time. The rate of decay also differs from one radioactive element to the next and is expressed as its half-life; that is, the time it takes for half of the parent atoms to decay to daughter atoms. If this is known, the relative proportion of parent and daughter atoms can be used to calculate the age of the parent element.

It was soon realized that radioactivity could be used to date rocks and, in 1905, Rutherford dated a uranium ore sample to be several hundred million years old. Since then, radiometric dating of rocks using many different radioactive elements has become increasingly routine, sensitive, sophisticated and reliable.

At its simplest, the age of a rock sample can be determined by measuring the abundances of radioactive parent and daughter atoms in it. Using the half-life, the age when the rock formed can be easily and precisely calculated if the material being dated contained no daughter atoms when it formed. However, when daughter atoms are not fully separated from the parent, dating is less precise. Fortunately, some parent-daughter pairs separate naturally during rock or mineral formation, so the daughter is excluded. The potassium-argon dating method makes use of this phenomenon.

One of the isotopes of potassium, potassium 40 (^{40}K, atomic mass = 40), is radioactive and decays to argon over a half-life of 1 250 million years. Since argon is a chemically inert gas, it is excluded when a rock or mineral containing potassium forms. But as time passes, ^{40}K atoms in the rock decay to argon atoms, which become trapped in the parent rock or mineral. Consequently, the rock's age can be determined by measuring the accumulated argon and the amount of ^{40}K remaining.

Another dating method involving daughter-free materials is based on the decay of uranium isotopes in the mineral zircon, which is fairly

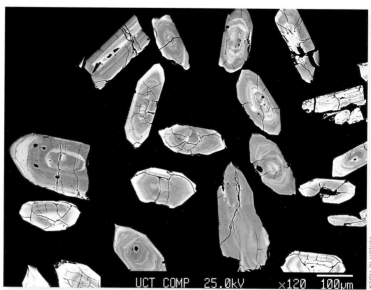

A laser or ion beam fired at zircon crystals such as these volatilizes atoms and releases uranium and lead in the vapour, which reveal the zircon's age.

UCT COMP   25.0kV   ×120   100μm

Anton le Roex

dyke

Carl Anhaeusser

The relative age of sedimentary rocks can be determined from the fact that younger layers lie above older layers. Here, a younger igneous dyke has intruded through the older sedimentary strata.

common in igneous rocks. There are two common uranium isotopes, uranium 235 (^{235}U) and uranium 238 (^{238}U), and each decays to a different isotope of lead (lead 207 [^{207}Pb] and lead 206 [^{206}Pb] respectively) with a different half-life. When a zircon crystal forms, uranium atoms readily become incorporated into its crystal structure because they resemble and replace zirconium atoms. Lead, on the other hand, is excluded, so a newly formed zircon crystal contains uranium but no lead. By measuring the amounts of ^{235}U, ^{238}U, ^{207}Pb and ^{206}Pb in the zircon, two identical ages can be calculated, thus providing a built-in check.

Zircon crystals are usually only a few millimetres in diameter, so sophisticated tools are needed to analyse them. In some instruments, an ion beam or powerful laser beam vaporizes some of the material, releasing uranium and lead atoms, which can be quantified using a mass spectrometer. From this, scientists can obtain very precise ages that vary by less than 1–2 million years in rocks that are 3 000 million years old.

It is essential in all dating methods that the rock in question must have formed at a specific time rather than over a protracted period, and it should not have been reheated since formation, since this may partially reset its radioactive clocks. Igneous and high-grade metamorphic rocks are

therefore the best candidates for dating, whereas sedimentary rocks present problems. Although they form at a specific time, their constituent minerals come from the weathering of older rocks. Dating the minerals would therefore reveal the ages of the older source rocks rather than the younger sedimentary rock.

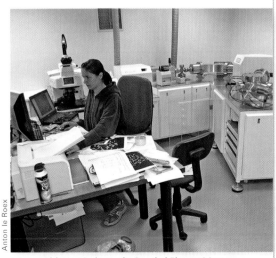

Anton le Roex

A Laser Ablation Inductively Coupled Plasma Mass Spectrometer (LA-ICP-MS) at the University of Cape Town is used to date mineral samples.

2 | EARTH'S CHANGING FACE

HAS A DAY ALWAYS LASTED 24 HOURS?

No, not always. The length of a day is determined by the time it takes for the Earth to complete one rotation on its axis, so the question can be rephrased: has the Earth's rate of rotation remained constant over time?

The Moon's gravitational pull on the Earth is significant and has to be taken into account when we analyse the Earth's movements. In fact, the Earth and Moon behave as a double planet system and rotate around a common centre of gravity. Movements of the Earth are therefore quite complex. It rotates on its axis once every 24 hours, while revolving around the Earth-Moon centre of gravity, or barycentre, once every 28 days. In addition, the Earth-Moon pair orbits the Sun once every 365 days.

MOVEMENTS OF THE EARTH AND MOON

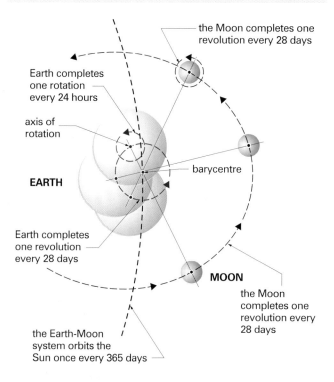

the Moon completes one revolution every 28 days

Earth completes one rotation every 24 hours

axis of rotation

EARTH

barycentre

Earth completes one revolution every 28 days

MOON

the Moon completes one revolution every 28 days

the Earth-Moon system orbits the Sun once every 365 days

The Earth and Moon rotate around a common centre of gravity, the barycentre, which lies 4 800 km from the centre of the Earth. They complete one revolution around the barycentre every 28 days. Simultaneously, the Earth rotates on its own axis once every 24 hours, and both the Earth and Moon orbit the Sun once every 365 days.

Tidal effects influence Earth movements and also have to be considered. The Moon's gravitational pull drags ocean water towards it, creating a tidal bulge on one side of the Earth. On the opposite side, an equal bulge is created by the centrifugal force of the Earth's rotation around the barycentre. The Sun also has a tidal effect, but it is much weaker because of the greater distance between the Sun and the Earth. Nevertheless, it either amplifies or mutes lunar tidal cycles. We experience a higher-than-average spring tide when the Sun's pull is in the same direction as the Moon's, or a smaller neap tide when it is perpendicular to the Moon's pull.

If the Earth did not spin on its axis, the tidal bulge would lie directly below the Moon and it would gradually move around the Earth as the Moon progressed along its orbit, completing a full circuit in 28 days. However, the daily rotation of the Earth on its axis complicates matters, because it means that the tidal bulges must complete one circuit of the Earth in 24 hours rather than 28 days, thus resulting in two high tides and two low tides each day. The tidal bulge is effectively going in the opposite direction to the Earth's rotation and it has to move rapidly to keep up. At the equator its speed is about 1 700 km per hour! This means that a lot of water has to flow backwards and forwards to keep the tidal bulge aligned with the Moon, but continents, especially Africa and South America, get in the way and slow the water down, in effect creating friction. The tidal bulge simply cannot keep up and lags behind its ideal position directly below the Moon by about 3°.

Tidal friction is imperceptibly slowing the Earth's rotation, while the offset of the tidal bulge causes a slight gravitational tug on the Moon, speeding up its rotation. This tug also contributes to slowing the Earth's rotation, but as the Moon gains rotational energy, it moves further away from Earth. Although minute, these changes can be measured. Laser reflectors placed on the Moon by the Apollo astronauts revealed that the

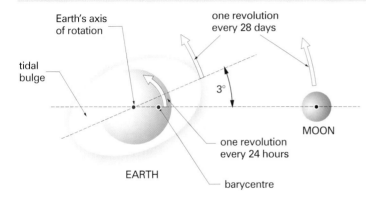

Earth's axis of rotation

one revolution every 28 days

tidal bulge

3°

MOON

one revolution every 24 hours

EARTH

barycentre

Gravitational attraction by the Moon pulls the ocean water upwards and towards it, creating a tidal bulge. This is counterpoised by a similar bulge on the opposite side of the Earth due to centrifugal force. The tidal bulge should theoretically always point directly towards the Moon as it orbits the Earth. However, the speed of the Earth's daily rotation and the position of continents complicates the way in which the tidal bulge follows the Moon, with the result that the tidal bulge is always about 3° ahead of where it should be. This is imperceptibly slowing the Earth's rotation and causing the Moon to recede from the Earth.

Moon is receding from Earth by 3.82 cm per year. Changes in the rate of the Earth's rotation have been noted by studying the time of total eclipses in ancient historical records, which show that an eclipse 2 000 years ago occurred about three hours earlier than predicted from the present rate of rotation. These observations answer the initial question, at least in part – days in the distant past were less than 24 hours.

But how can day length and the number of days in a year be determined in the geological past? Sedimentary rocks that were deposited under suitable conditions can reveal the answer. One such condition is provided by river deltas with strong tidal flows that were sheltered from intense wave activity. Sediment brought into such deltas by rivers is drawn into deeper water by the ebb tide and deposited as a discrete layer. Each ebb tide deposits a single layer, typically about a centimetre thick, but thicker during spring tides and thinner during neap tides. Rocks showing these characteristics are known as tidalites and the layers of varying thickness within them record the lunar tidal cycle. Annual cycles reflecting changing seasons are

also preserved, since more sediment is delivered during a rainy season, making the layers even thicker. By studying such deposits it is possible to determine the day length, the number of days in a lunar month and the number of months in a year. Mathematical analysis of historical Earth and Moon orbits is used to supplement and refine measurements obtained from these tidalites.

Such measurements reveal that 620 million years ago there were 21.9 hours in a day and about 400 days in a year, divided into 13.1 lunar months. Data from older rock suites is less secure, but suggests that 2 450 million years ago a day was about 19 hours long, and that there were 457 days and 14.5 lunar months in a year. Day length 3 300 million years ago may have been as short as 14 hours.

The Moon's rate of recession from Earth seems to have accelerated over time, from about 1.24 cm per year 2 450 million years ago, to the current 3.82 cm per year. The rate of recession has probably also fluctuated, possibly due to variable tidal friction brought about by the changing positions of the continents.

Under the right conditions, sedimentary deposition can record tidal cycles, with each tide depositing a very thin, single sedimentary layer. Such rocks, called tidalites, can be used to estimate the day length, lunar month and the number of days in the year in the distant past.

neap

spring

neap

Ken Eriksson

WERE AFRICA AND SOUTH AMERICA ONCE JOINED?

THE BREAKUP OF SUPERCONTINENT PANGAEA

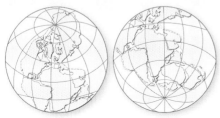

190 million years ago

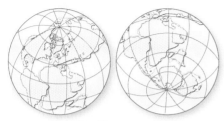

120 million years ago

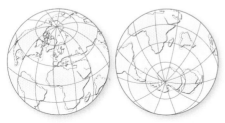

60 million years ago

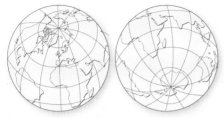

10 million years ago

About 150 million years ago, all the world's continents were joined together as a supercontinent named Pangaea, which was counterpoised by a great ocean, Panthalassa. Pangaea began to break up about 140 million years ago and the fragments dispersed around the globe.

Perhaps the most striking aspect of a map of the Atlantic Ocean is how well the east coast of South America and the west coast of Africa fit together. An even better fit is obtained if the edges of their continental shelves are matched. The reason for this is that South America and Africa are fragments of what was once a single supercontinent called Gondwana, which included all the southern hemisphere continents, as well as India. The northern hemisphere continents formed a similar supercontinent, known as Laurasia. For a time these two huge landmasses were joined together to form Pangaea, which was counterpoised by a great ocean, Panthalassa.

Pangaea began to break up about 140 million years ago, starting with the formation of rift valleys, such as seen today in East Africa. With the widening of the rifts, the ocean flooded in to form narrow oceans rather like the modern Red Sea. Separation continued and ultimately produced vast oceans such as the Atlantic. The expansion of such new oceans occurred at the expense of the Panthalassa Ocean, which shrank in size, leaving only the Pacific Ocean as a remnant of its previous vast size.

So are the continents still moving? High-precision survey methods based on the satellite-based Global Positioning System show that they are. South America continues to recede from Africa at about four centimetres per year. This survey method has brought us a long way from the first serious attempt to prove that continents drift around the surface of the Earth, as first proposed in the early twentieth century by the German geologist, Alfred Wegener. By linking the geological formations and similarities of South America and Africa, for example, the physical evidence for continental drift was strong. However, no-one could conceive of a force powerful enough to move huge landmasses around, so Wegener's concept of continental drift was ignored for many years.

His idea remained in the realms of fringe science until the 1960s, when topographic maps of the ocean floors became available (see page 136) and new discoveries were made about the nature of the rocks forming the oceanic crust (see page 32). These provided key clues and the old ideas about continental drift were revamped, emerging in a new form as the theory of plate tectonics.

According to this theory, the Earth's outer skin or lithosphere is divided into great rafts, or plates,

EARTH'S MOVING CONTINENTS

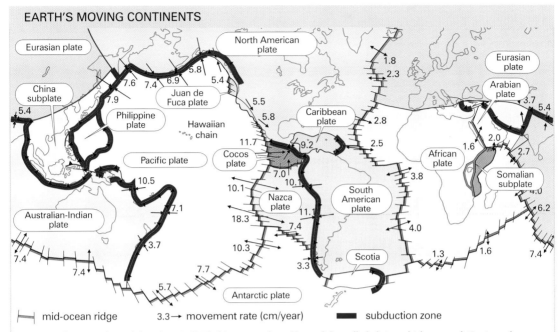

| mid-ocean ridge | 3.3→ movement rate (cm/year) | subduction zone |

The Earth's outer skin or lithosphere is divided into a number of large slabs, called plates, which move relative to each other. Boundaries between the plates are the most geologically active regions of the world, and most of the Earth's earthquakes and volcanoes occur in these zones.

which float on the underlying asthenosphere and are in constant motion relative to one another. At mid-ocean ridges, the lithosphere tears open and new oceanic crust is made, while elsewhere, old oceanic crust slides down into the deep mantle and is recycled – a process known as subduction. Continental crust has a lower density than oceanic crust and is not subducted to any great extent, so only oceanic crust is recycled at subduction zones. In effect, therefore, the continents are indeed drifting, shifted around like flotsam by the constantly recirculating oceanic crust, and they typically move a few centimetres each year – about the rate at which finger nails grow.

FORMATION OF THE ATLANTIC OCEAN

The lithosphere of the Earth is fairly rigid and floats on the underlying, fluid-like, plastic and deformable asthenosphere, whose movement is driven by heat loss from Earth's interior. How this happens is unclear, but one possibility involves convective currents in the asthenosphere, which may drag the lithosphere along, as shown here. New ocean crust is created at mid-ocean ridges and old ocean crust is recycled as it plunges down into the asthenosphere, forming a kind of conveyor on which the continents ride.

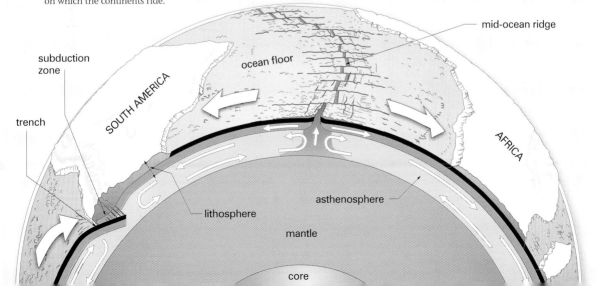

WHY IS THE EARTH DIVIDED INTO CONTINENTS AND OCEANS?

Rocks that form the continents are different from those that form the ocean floors and hence the division of the Earth into continents and oceans cannot be a matter of chance. Continental rock (granite) consists of the minerals alkali feldspar (sodium, potassium and aluminium silicate) and quartz (silicon dioxide), while ocean floor rock (basalt) consists of the minerals pyroxene (calcium, iron and magnesium silicate) and calcium feldspar. They differ in density and thickness – continental rock has an average density of about 2.7 g/cm³ and an average thickness of about 35 km, compared to the average oceanic rock density of about 2.9 g/cm³ and average thickness of 6–7 km.

These rock types form the Earth's crust, which is underlain by mantle material that consists mainly of the minerals olivine (iron, magnesium silicate) and pyroxene and has a density of 3.3 g/cm³. The upper 100 km of the mantle is relatively cool and thus rigid, and this layer, together with the Earth's crust makes up the lithosphere. Temperature in the Earth increases with depth and over a 200-km-thick zone below the lithosphere (known as the asthenosphere) the mantle is very close to its melting temperature and is consequently very deformable or plastic, like putty. The more rigid rocks of the lithosphere essentially float on this plastic layer.

An object with a low density is more buoyant and therefore floats higher on water, for example, than an object with a higher density. However, if the density of the object exceeds that of water, it will of course sink. For example, a block of polystyrene floats higher on water than a block of pinewood of the same size, because pine is much denser than polystyrene, but less so than water, so it too floats. Furthermore, a thicker block of pine will expose more wood above the water line than a thinner one. It is not unexpected, therefore, that the thicker, lower-density continental crust should float higher on the asthenosphere than the thinner and denser oceanic crust. However, the situation is more complex, because sea water covers the denser oceanic crust and just fills the ocean basins (average depth 4 000 m), leaving the continents to project above sea level by just a few hundred metres on

Two types of geological terrain exist on Earth: the continents and the ocean basins. On average, continents stand about 4 000 m higher than the ocean floors and rise only a few hundred metres above sea level, so Earth has just enough water to fill the ocean basins.

OUTER LAYERS OF THE EARTH

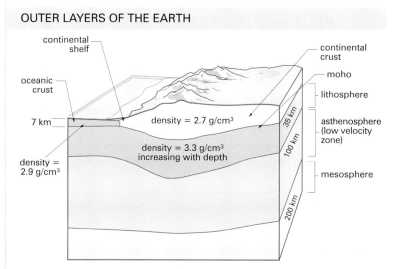

The Earth's two types of crust differ in density and thickness, as shown here. Beneath the crust is a layer of mantle rock which, together with the crust, forms the lithosphere. This floats on the putty-like and plastic asthenosphere.

PRESSURE EQUALIZATION BELOW THE CRUST

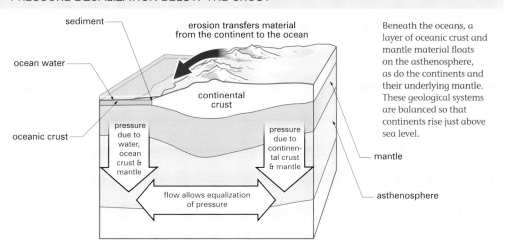

sediment

erosion transfers material from the continent to the ocean

ocean water

continental crust

oceanic crust

pressure due to water, ocean crust & mantle

pressure due to continental crust & mantle

flow allows equalization of pressure

mantle

asthenosphere

Beneath the oceans, a layer of oceanic crust and mantle material floats on the asthenosphere, as do the continents and their underlying mantle. These geological systems are balanced so that continents rise just above sea level.

average. Is this a coincidence, or does it have a deeper significance?

To answer this question we need to consider the lithosphere in more detail, and especially the force, or pressure, it exerts on the underlying asthenosphere. The pressure exerted by the continental crust and its underlying lithospheric mantle is equal to the pressure exerted by the oceanic crust plus sea water and its underlying lithospheric mantle.

The land surface is subjected to a relentless attack by water, wind and ice, which eventually transform the rocks into gravel, sand and mud that are transported by rivers into the oceans where this material is deposited. The continental crust is therefore constantly being reduced in thickness and, because it is floating, it rises as it becomes thinner, so reducing the pressure on the asthenosphere. In theory, continents should reach a point where they are eroded down to sea level and exert the same pressure as the oceanic crust and the overlying ocean. It turns out

that this point is reached when the thickness of continental crust is 35 km, just as we find it on Earth.

In practice, erosion rates become progressively slower as the continents get lower, so their interiors usually remain a couple of hundred metres above sea level. This is why vast areas of North America, Russia and Siberia, northern South America and Australia lie at such elevations.

So the fact that the Earth possesses continents and oceans, and that it has just enough sea water to more or less exactly fill the ocean basins, is thus not a coincidence at all, but a consequence of the dynamic interplay between the different types of crust, the putty-like nature of the asthenosphere and the processes of erosion.

The islands that make up the Seychelles are, in fact, microcontinents formed by continental crust. They are therefore unlike most other deep-ocean islands, which typically are formed by the peaks of tall volcanoes.

Fiona McIntosh / IOA

33

HOW DID EARTH'S OCEANS AND CONTINENTS FORM?

The Earth formed about 4 540 million years ago in the hot inner regions of a gas and dust cloud known as the Solar Nebula (see page 12) and grew by the amalgamation of clumps of cosmic dust called planetesimals. About 4 530 million years ago, when it had reached about 60% of its present size, fledgling Earth was hit a glancing blow by a planetesimal about the size of Mars, which vaporized some of Earth's outermost layer. This vapour condensed to form the Moon. The Earth's growth continued for a few more tens of millions of years, essentially ending with the Late Bombardment by small planetesimals about 3 900 million years ago. Impact scars from this violent bombardment are still visible on the lunar surface as dark circular patches.

Earth's growth process was so violent that the Earth may have remained molten during the early stages, but as the tempo of growth slowed and the planet began to cool and solidify, it is likely that a crust formed. We do not know what this crust was made of, but it may have been similar to the ancient crust on the Moon, which consists mainly of calcium aluminium silicate (anorthosite).

If water was present on Earth at this stage, it would have occurred entirely as vapour in the atmosphere. As the Earth cooled further, however, rain began to fall and the first oceans appeared, possibly as early as 4 400 million years ago. Where did this water come from? Some scientists think that chemically combined water may have been released from Earth's rocks (called degassing) by the intense heat of bombardment; others favour an extraterrestrial origin, in which the water was delivered in the form of planetesimals from the cooler, outer regions of the Solar Nebula, which would have been enriched in water (see page 14).

The Earth's atmosphere then consisted largely of carbon dioxide and the atmospheric pressure was probably considerably higher than it is today (see page 54). Although the Sun was cooler, the greenhouse effect of the atmosphere may have resulted in higher surface temperatures than we are familiar with today. Large extraterrestrial bodies colliding with the Earth may have partially – or even completely – vaporized the early oceans from time to time, especially during the Late Bombardment. From about 3 800 million years ago, however, the bombardment from space waned and conditions became more settled, and it is likely that oceans have been a permanent feature of the Earth since then. The oldest known sedimentary rocks, found in the Amitsoq gneiss in Greenland, date from this time.

Studies of the isotopic composition of hydrogen in the atmospheres of Earth, Venus and Mars indicate that all three planets have substantially less water than they originally had. In the case of Earth, it may have lost the

EARTH'S FIRST CONTINENT

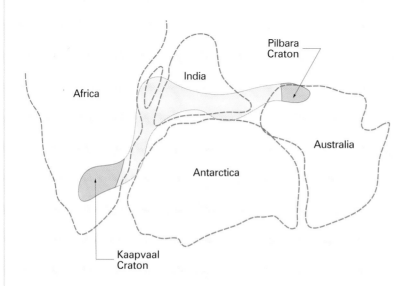

The oldest sizable continent, named Ur (shaded), formed between 3 650 and 3 000 million years ago. Of this, the Kaapvaal Craton (South Africa) and the Pilbara Craton (Australia) have been well studied.

Fragments of ancient ocean crust within the Kaapvaal Craton include pillow lavas that were formed when basalt lava erupted under the sea.

Rocks in the Barberton area of Mpumalanga formed part of the Earth's first known continent, named Ur, and are among the oldest on the planet.

equivalent of a kilometre of ocean depth. The early anorthositic crust would have been more homogeneous than the present crust, and with more water in the oceans there was probably very little land. Perhaps the only land would have been confined to a few islands formed by the peaks of large volcanoes.

The Earth's continents are made of a distinctive rock type called granite that is formed during the plate tectonic process. When basaltic crust and mantle material that have become hydrated by interaction with ocean water are drawn down into the Earth by subduction and subsequently heated, they undergo partial melting to produce granite. Granitic rock made its appearance as early as 4 400 million years ago, providing evidence that oceans were present, that plate tectonics had started and that a continental crust was beginning to form.

Geologists can date the advent of granite at 4 400 million years ago from a grain of the mineral zircon, discovered in Western Australia, that was derived from granite. The oldest known actual granitic rock has been dated at 4 100 million years and occurs in Canada, while the oldest known true continent is represented by the Kaapval Craton of South Africa and the Pilbara Craton of Australia, both of which include slivers of basaltic oceanic crust, indicating that by this time basaltic and granitic crusts were distinctly separated.

So it seems likely that the granitic crust started forming some 4 400 million years ago, giving rise to the first microcontinents. The rarity of granite masses older than 3 500 million years suggests that these micro-continents were very small and widely scattered around the globe. Volcanic islands probably vastly outnumbered them to begin with,

but over time they grew in number and began to be swept together by plate tectonic processes. Thus the first true, sizable continents, such as the Kaapvaal and Pilbara Cratons, were formed, but even these were minute in comparison to modern continents which today form about one third of the Earth's crust.

MOON

Whitish areas are the Moon's early crust, dating from 4 500 million years ago; they contrast sharply with the darker coloured, younger basalt of the lunar 'seas'.

HOW DO MOUNTAINS FORM?

Volcanic mountains can be extremely high, such as the 3 426 m Mount Hood in Oregon, USA.

Terence McCarthy

One person's mountain is another's molehill, so for someone who grew up in the Alps, the Magaliesberg would seem like a range of low hills. A mountain is really defined by local topographic contrast rather than by absolute height above sea level. The summit of Ben Nevis, the highest mountain in the United Kingdom, is 1 343 m above sea level, almost 500 m lower than the elevation of Johannesburg (1 800 m). In fact, even the crest of the Magaliesberg, at about 1 700 m, is lower than Johannesburg, but we don't consider Johannesburg to be on a mountain.

Just as mountains differ in size, they vary, too, in how they form. A volcanic mountain forms when lava and volcanic debris erupt from a vent located more or less at its apex. There are two kinds of volcanoes. One has silica-rich lava and grows mainly by avalanches of hot, fragmental material, with occasional flows. Known as stratovolcanoes, these have a layered internal structure and slopes of about 30°, and can grow to a height of about 5 000 m, generally occurring on land. Mount Fuji in Japan and Mount Hood in the USA are typical examples.

The other kind of volcano is formed by the eruption of very fluid lava with low silica content. It ejects mainly lava that flows rapidly away from the vent, cooling and hardening as it goes. These volcanoes have more gentle slopes, typically of about 10°, and they occur in the oceans, forming volcanic islands such as Hawaii. The mountains they build are truly massive, although most of their bulk is usually hidden beneath the sea. The tallest mountain in the world, Mauna Kea in Hawaii, is of this type and rises to a height of 10 000 m above its base, of which 5 500 m are below sea level.

Some of the most impressive mountains in the world occur in long chains. A notable example is the Cordillera range along the west coast of the Americas, extending from Alaska to the tip of South America. This mountain chain was formed when the slow westerly moving American tectonic plate collided with the Pacific tectonic plate. This movement also created the Atlantic Ocean, which is still widening (see page 30).

When two plates collide, one may slide down beneath the other, partially melting the subducting plate as it does so and forming silica-rich volcanoes such as Mount Hood. Sediment on the ocean floor is scraped off the descending plate and becomes compressed against the leading edge of the over-riding plate. The sedimentary layers thicken and become folded, producing fold mountains. The combination of volcano formation and the thickening and folding of rock layers has created the great elevation of the Cordilleras. Such high mountain ranges are sculpted into their characteristic jagged shapes, however, by the erosive power of running water, wind and ice at high elevations.

Terence McCarthy

The locally impressive Magaliesberg northwest of Johannesburg rise 1 700 m above sea level, but just 300 m above the surrounding terrain. Lower than Johannesburg, which lies at 1 800 m, the Magaliesberg, seen here on a hazy winter morning, are simply low hills by world standards.

FORMATION OF THE ANDEAN MOUNTAINS

Where tectonic plates converge, subduction zones create fold mountains and volcanoes. Fold mountains form from ocean floor sediment, while volcanoes result from melting of the subducting plate and surrounding mantle.

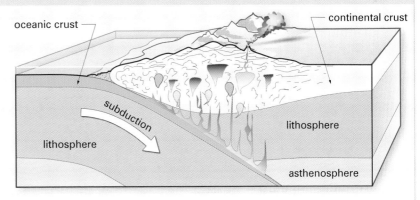

The mountains of the southern Cape in South Africa are the eroded roots of fold mountains that formed in a similar way (see page 102). Occasionally, moving plates can bring two continents into a head-on collision, creating super-high ranges such as the Alps and the Himalayan range (see page 38).

The vertical displacement of the Earth's crust along large fractures or faults can create dramatic contrasts in elevation, such as in the Basin and Range province in the mid-west and southwest of the USA. These often form in response to stretching of the Earth's crust. The up-faulted blocks (horsts) are sculpted by erosion into rugged mountain ranges and the resulting sediment is deposited in the down-faulted areas (grabens). These often have internal drainage systems and in more arid areas, such as Death Valley in California, they commonly result in saltpans.

In southern Africa, most of the mountain ranges formed quite differently. The interior consists largely of a broad, gently undulating plateau that rises from about 1 000 m in the west to 1 800 m in the east. It is bordered by the Great Escarpment, which formed after the break-up of the supercontinent Gondwana, when southern Africa was more or less surrounded by rift valleys. Erosion carved the shoulders of the rifts, pushing them back to give the present escarpment its shape. In the east, where it is known as the Drakensberg, the escarpment is particularly impressive, with local geology causing it to form almost vertical walls in places that are more than 1 200 m high.

Several mountain ranges occur on the plateau itself, the most impressive of which rises more than 1 000 m above the plateau to form the Lesotho Highlands or Maluti Mountains. Others – notably the Soutpansberg, Waterberg, Magaliesberg, Langeberg and Asbesberg – attain an elevation of only a few hundred metres above the plateau. They are all composed of very hard rock that has resisted erosion while the surrounding softer rock was worn away.

MOUNTAINS FORMED BY STRETCHING OF THE CRUST

Stretching of Earth's crust may cause crustal blocks (horsts) to rise, but others (grabens) to descend. Grabens collect material eroded from the horsts. Parallel ridges and valleys result. The Death Valley region in the USA is a good example, where peaks can rise up to 3 400 m above adjacent valley floors.

WHY ARE THE HIGHEST MOUNTAIN PEAKS IN THE HIMALAYAN RANGE?

It is no coincidence that most of the world's highest peaks are located in the Himalayan range, which started forming when India collided with Asia about 15 million years ago. India was once attached to the east coast of Africa and was part of the southern supercontinent, Gondwana. When Gondwana began to break up about 140 million years ago, the India-Antarctica-Australia portion separated from Africa-South America, forming the Indian Ocean. India separated from Antarctica about 40 million years later and started to move north towards a subduction zone along the southern boundary of Eurasia.

The Tethys Sea, which lay between Gondwana and the northern supercontinent, Laurasia, began to shrink, and the sediments that had accumulated on its floor were scraped off and crumpled up along the southern margin of the Eurasian plate as the underlying lithosphere was subducted (see page 36). Volcanoes formed along the boundary in southern Asia and, in conjunction with the folded sedimentary strata, they formed a high mountain range similar to the Andes. About 15 million years ago the Tethys Sea finally closed as the Indian continent collided with the Eurasian continent.

The impact caused great thickening of the continental crust along the collision zone, producing elevated terrain in the form of the Himalayan range and the Tibetan Plateau. The region is elevated because continental crust, being less dense, floats on the underlying denser mantle material, and thicker crust stands higher than thinner crust – just as big ice cubes project higher above the surface of your drink than small ice cubes. The net result is that this region has the highest average elevation on Earth, so it is not surprising that many of the world's highest mountains are found there.

SUPERCONTINENT PANGAEA

India was once part of Gondwana, and joined to Africa and Antarctica. When Gondwana began to break up 140 million years ago, India moved northwards, thereby closing the Tethys Sea.

ELEVATION ACROSS TIBET

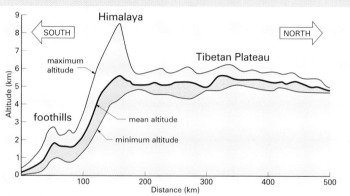

Most of the world's highest mountains lie in the Himalayan Range, but its average height is slightly lower than that of the Tibetan Plateau to the north.

THE INDIA–ASIA COLLISION

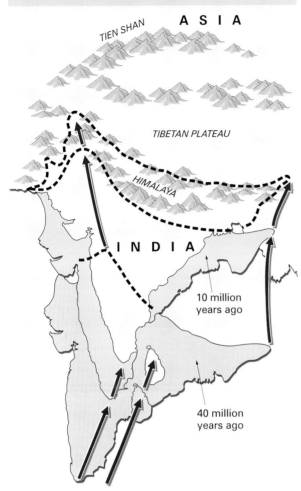

The Indian and Asian continents collided 15 million years ago. India continues to plough northwards at 5 cm per year, still pushing up the Himalayan range and Tibet.

THE WORLD'S 10 HIGHEST MOUNTAINS

1. Everest, Himalaya, Nepal/Tibet	8 850 m
2. K2, Karakoram, Pakistan/China	8 611 m
3. Kanchenjunga, Himalaya, Nepal/	8 586 m
4. Lhotse I, Himalaya, Nepal/Tibet	8 516 m
5. Makalu, Himalaya, Nepal/Tibet	8 463 m
6. Cho Oyu, Himalaya, Nepal/Tibet	8 201 m
7. Dhaulagiri, Himalaya, Nepal	8 167 m
8. Manaslu I, Himalaya, Nepal	8 163 m
9. Nanga Parbat, Karakoram, Pakistan	8 125 m
10. Annapurna, Himalaya, Nepal	8 091 m

Some scientists believe that an additional factor may have led to the formation of super-high mountain peaks in the Himalayan range. The high terrain of the region intercepts moisture-laden air from the Indian Ocean, forcing it to rise and cool. This process produces abundant precipitation in the form of rain and snow on the southern section of the Tibetan region (India's monsoon rains). Heavy rain and snow, combined with high relief, accelerate erosion. As the mountains are eroded, the crust forming them becomes thinner and therefore more buoyant, so the mountains rise, but by less than the amount eroded; thus the average elevation decreases. However, the rate of erosion is slower on the mountain peaks than in the valleys because the valleys carry rivers, and glaciers at higher elevation, both of which are powerfully erosive. So while on average the continental crust is getting thinner and the average elevation is decreasing, peaks, where the erosion rate is slower, continue to rise. This process increases the difference in elevation between peaks and valleys and results in relatively very high peaks that accentuate the extreme height of the highest mountains.

The southern edge of the Tibetan Plateau experiences the most precipitation and has the highest mountain peaks (the Himalayan range) as well as the greatest topographic contrast between high and low ground. Nevertheless, its average elevation is slightly less than that of the drier Tibetan Plateau to the north.

South Africans Vaughan de la Harpe and Sean Disney on the summit of Mount Everest, 24 May 2006.

René Hochreiter

HOW ARE VOLCANOES FORMED?

Volcanoes are not uniformly spread around the Earth. Most are found in distinct belts such as the one around the Pacific Ocean, which has been called the 'Ring of Fire'. Other volcanoes are isolated and usually occur in oceans, where they form islands such as Hawaii, Iceland and St Helena. Detailed investigation of the ocean floor has revealed that there are also many undersea volcanoes, which are present in an extensive system of rift valleys, known as mid-ocean ridge systems.

Broadly speaking, volcanoes are of two types and they differ in the chemical composition of the lava they erupt: lavas having lower silica are termed 'basalt', while those having high silica content are called 'rhyolite and andesite'.

High-silica lavas (65–74%) melt at about 1 000°C and are extremely viscous, like cold golden syrup. Their volcanoes have the classic conical shape, like Mount Fuji in Japan and Mount St Helens in the USA. The viscous magma tends to release its dissolved gases explosively, producing vast quantities of volcanic ash, which consists of minute particles of lava. Rather than flowing, the lava tends to erupt from the volcano's summit in the form of avalanches of red-hot material that cascade down the slopes (called pyroclastic flows), maintaining the conical shape.

Volcanoes of this type are known as stratovolcanoes and are made up of layers of ash, volcanic rubble and occasional lava. Now and again they explode catastrophically, as Krakatoa did in Indonesia in 1883 and Mount St Helens in 1980.

The other type of volcano produces basaltic lava that has a lower silica content (about 50%) and is richer in calcium, iron and magnesium. Basaltic lava erupts at about 1 200°C; dissolved gases escape easily as the lava emerges from the volcano, and little ash is produced. This type of lava has a relatively low viscosity and flows readily, like motor oil, cooling as it goes. The resulting shield volcano is composed mainly of lava and has gentle slopes. Sometimes, such as in Iceland, basaltic lava pours out of long cracks in what is known as a fissure eruption, without forming an obvious volcano.

The world's volcanoes form as a result of plate tectonic processes (see page 30). Rhyolite and andesite are most commonly produced at subduction zones where the ocean floor, together with its underlying lithospheric mantle, plunges down into the asthenosphere. There the subducted plate is heated up and gives off volatile substances (mainly water and carbon dioxide) that it acquired while at the Earth's surface. Acting as a kind of

THE WORLD'S ACTIVE VOLCANOES

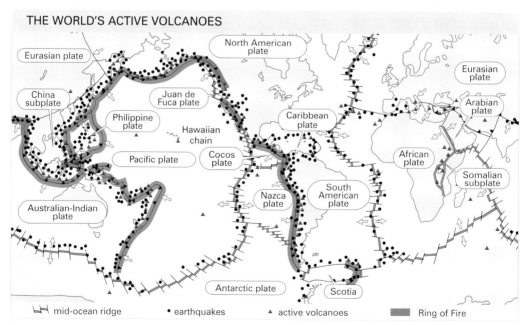

Eurasian plate
North American plate
China subplate
Juan de Fuca plate
Eurasian plate
Philippine plate
Arabian plate
Hawaiian chain
Caribbean plate
Pacific plate
Cocos plate
African plate
Somalian subplate
Nazca plate
South American plate
Australian-Indian plate
Antarctic plate
Scotia

⊢⊣ mid-ocean ridge   • earthquakes   ▲ active volcanoes   ▨ Ring of Fire

Most volcanoes occur along the edges of tectonic plates, especially around the active Pacific Ocean rim. But some, such as Hawaii, are isolated and formed when deep columns of hot magma broke through Earth's crust.

Volcanoes above tectonic subduction zones produce viscous lava and may erupt violently, as did Mount St Helens in May 1980, when its peak and side were blown away. The devastation is still visible.

flux, these substances promote the melting of the surrounding mantle, and possibly the subducted oceanic crust too, which results in rhyolite and andesite. Such volcanoes therefore occur along regions where the Earth's plates are converging, mostly around the rim of the Pacific Ocean.

Basalt is produced when pressure on the hot mantle is reduced, usually when the Earth's more rigid outer skin, or lithosphere, stretches and tears. Molten basalt shoots into the cracks in the stretched crust and lithosphere, and some erupts onto the surface. The zones of stretching and tearing, which manifest themselves as rift valleys, occur mostly on the ocean floors but occasionally also at the surface, as in the case of Iceland and East Africa's Rift Valley. Basalt volcanoes also form oceanic islands such as Hawaii, apparently when columns of very hot mantle (called plumes) rise from the core-mantle boundary. As the column approaches the surface, the reduced pressure results in partial melting and basalt is produced. Huge volcanoes can be created by mantle plumes; for example, the volcanic island of Hawaii is 10 km tall. A mantle plume rising beneath a continent can melt the crust, giving rise to large and explosive rhyolite volcanoes. The Yellowstone volcano in the USA is believed to be of this type.

Volcanoes can be classified as active (giving off lava, ash or fumes); dormant (showing no activity for centuries); and extinct (being inactive for tens of thousands of years). However, dormant volcanoes may sometimes suddenly spring to life. Twelve of the sixteen largest explosive eruptions of the nineteenth and twentieth centuries involved volcanoes that were considered long-since dormant. Even though the active life of an individual volcano may be measured in millions of years, all volcanoes ultimately become extinct because the movement of the Earth's plates moves them away from their source of magma. When this happens, the magma has to find an alternative path to the surface. The best-documented instance of this is the Hawaiian mantle plume, which has been active for at least 70 million years and has left a chain of extinct volcanoes (mostly submerged) from Hawaii northwards to the Aleutian Islands, a distance of 3 500 km.

Basalt lava is sometimes sufficiently fluid to drain away from beneath its outer, solid crust, leaving a hollow lava tube, such as here at the Lava Beds National Monument in California, USA.

WHY DO SO FEW SERIOUS EARTHQUAKES OCCUR IN SOUTH AFRICA?

Some regions of the world are prone to very severe earthquakes, but in South Africa, large seismic events are rare. The most severe ones recorded were the 6.5 and 6.2 magnitude earthquakes of September 1969 and April 1970 respectively, which seriously damaged buildings in Ceres and Tulbagh in the southwestern Cape.

Most earthquakes arise when accumulated stresses in the Earth's crust are suddenly released, as when a dry twig that is being bent finally snaps. The released energy causes the ground to vibrate, sometimes so severely that buildings collapse. The Earth's cool, rigid outer skin, or lithosphere, is broken up into several large segments, called plates, which are constantly moving (see page 30). Stress builds up at plate boundaries until its sudden release causes an earthquake – usually most severe where plates converge. However, processes operating at the boundaries of plates also create stresses in their interior, sometimes resulting in earthquakes far from plate boundaries.

The African continent lies on the African plate, which in the north is currently colliding with the Eurasian plate. This collision has resulted in the formation of high mountains across southern Europe, including the Alps. Elsewhere, the African plate is surrounded by spreading zones in the form of mid-ocean ridges that extend from the Red Sea southwards through the Indian Ocean and across the South Atlantic and then northwards through the Atlantic Ocean. These plate boundaries are subject to regular earthquakes.

A rift, named the East African Rift Valley, has developed within the interior of the African plate. It commenced about 20 million years ago at the southern end of the Red Sea and appears to be propagating southwards into the plate. Earthquakes and volcanic activity are common in the northern section of the East African Rift, where it is clearly defined. Towards the south, the definition of the rift is less clear, and based on the distribution of earthquakes, it appears to split into several branches. One branch passes through central Mozambique and then offshore, extending south parallel to the KwaZulu-Natal coastline. Another passes in a southwesterly direction across Zambia and northern Botswana into Namibia. It is believed that these incipient cracks may develop into rift valleys in the distant future. There is a third, more contentious line of earthquake activity, which some regard as another incipient rift. This extends from Zambia southwards along the eastern escarpment of southern Africa as far as Lesotho, where it turns west, passing through Jagersfontein (a seismically active locality) and Namaqualand. Some scientists, however, consider this belt of seismic activity along the escarpment to be caused by topographic readjustments taking place there.

As the major plate boundaries lie well outside South Africa's borders, there are few earthquakes in the interior. However, the region is not totally earthquake-free, probably because stresses are transmitted

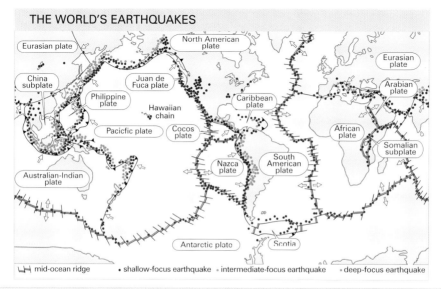

THE WORLD'S EARTHQUAKES

Eurasian plate
North American plate
Eurasian plate
China subplate
Juan de Fuca plate
Arabian plate
Philippine plate
Caribbean plate
Hawaiian chain
Pacific plate
Cocos plate
African plate
Somalian subplate
Nazca plate
South American plate
Australian-Indian plate
Antarctic plate
Scotia

⊢⊣ mid-ocean ridge   • shallow-focus earthquake   • intermediate-focus earthquake   • deep-focus earthquake

Most of the world's earthquakes occur along tectonic plate boundaries, with the most severe occurring where plates converge. Earthquakes are relatively rare in the interiors of plates.

from plate margins into the interior. For example, actively growing ocean ridges surround southern Africa, causing inwardly directed horizontal pressure. In addition, incipient rifts are developing to the north across Zambia and Botswana and to the east off the coast of KwaZulu-Natal, contributing additional horizontal stresses in the interior's crust. These horizontal stresses periodically cause local slippage along old lines of weakness or faults, resulting in small earthquakes that mostly go unnoticed. Occasionally, the slippage is more dramatic, as in the case of the Ceres-Tulbagh earthquakes, which were probably caused by movement along part of the Worcester fault. The seismic

The Star

On 8 December 1976, Welkom in Free State province was rocked by a magnitude 5.2 earthquake when mining activity triggered movement along a natural fault, causing extensive damage.

activity at Jagersfontein and through Namaqualand could be related to these stresses.

The most pronounced seismic activity in South Africa is actually human induced and arises as a result of deep-level gold mining, as the dense clusters of earthquakes around the gold-mining centres indicate. The average depth of mining is about two kilometres, but in some areas mines are as deep as 4 kms. The workings are subjected to huge pressure, which results in the slow constriction of mined spaces (voids) as mining proceeds. Occasionally, a mine void closes instantly in events known as rock bursts, releasing energy in the form of seismic waves. Mining activity may also trigger movement along natural fractures in the rock.

MAGNITUDE	EFFECT
1 to 3	Imperceptible to humans
3.5 to 4.2	Equivalent to vibrations caused by a passing truck; felt by people
4.3 to 4.8	Rocks loose objects; felt by someone walking
4.9 to 5.4	Causes suspended objects to sway and objects to fall off shelves
5.5 to 6.1	Causes walls to crack and may damage plaster
6.2 to 6.4	Causes brick chimneys to fall and damages poorly built structures
6.5 to 6.9	Causes some structures to collapse and cracks the ground
7 to 7.3	Bends railway lines, severely cracks the ground and destroys many structures
7.4 to 8.1	Leaves few buildings or bridges standing
Above 8.1	Causes the ground to oscillate in huge waves, throwing objects into the air and levelling virtually all structures

EARTHQUAKES OF SOUTHERN AFRICA

Seismic activity is continuously monitored and mapped by the Council for Geoscience using its network of seismometers. Seismic activity clearly defines the East African Rift System. Within South Africa, most natural seismic activity occurs near Ceres and Jagersfontein. The gold-producing areas show strong seismic activity as a result of deep-level mining activities.

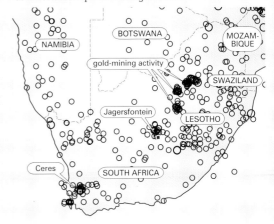

WILL AFRICA'S RIFT VALLEY FRAGMENT THE CONTINENT?

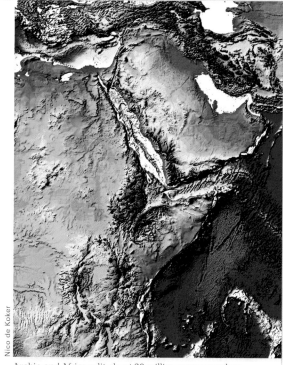

Nico de Koker

Arabia and Africa split about 20 million years ago when rifting opened the Red Sea and the Gulf of Aden. A third branch of the same rift produced the East African Rift Valley.

The East African Rift Valley is a great tear in the African continent that is widening by about 6 mm per year. A reminder of the constant relative movement of the Earth's plates, the Rift Valley started forming about 20 million years ago at the southern end of the Red Sea and has since extended progressively southward into Africa.

It is not clear what caused this specific tear, but one popular theory proposes that it was initiated by a plume of hot material from deep within the Earth that rose beneath the point where the Red Sea, the Gulf of Aden and the Rift Valley meet. If so, this hot material would cause the Earth's rigid outer layer, or lithosphere, to soften and bulge before finally splitting into three tears, or rifts, at about 120° to one another, creating what is known as a triple junction. The Red Sea and Gulf of Aden branches are far more active than the East African Rift and are spreading at about 1.6 and 2 cm per year respectively.

Rifting occurs by stretching in the deeper, hotter and more plastic region of the lithosphere and by cracking and slipping in the upper, cooler and more brittle parts. As the split widens and the lithosphere thins, the centre collapses, forming a rift valley such as the East African Rift, which often hosts lakes. Molten rock from the Earth's interior may rise along fractures in the thinned crust, producing volcanoes, while fracturing results in the release of energy, giving rise to earthquakes. By mapping the distribution of features such as lakes, volcanoes, fractures and earthquakes, it is possible to work out exactly where the rifting is taking place.

The East African Rift has effectively split the African plate, forming two subplates; the Nubian subplate to the west and the Somalian subplate

RIFT VALLEY FORMATION

1. Uplift occurs along the incipient rift zone.

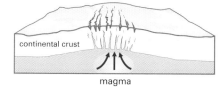

2. Collapse of the centre of the uplift occurs, forming a rift valley.

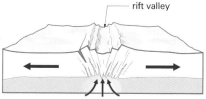

3. The rift valley widens and oceanic crust forms in its floor. The sea floods in and a new ocean is born.

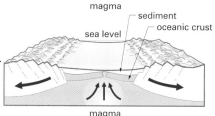

Continental rifts form when hot magma wells up and bulges beneath the crust, which stretches, fractures and collapses, creating a rift valley. Rising magma widens the rift, forming ocean crust, and sea floods in, creating a new ocean.

MANTLE PLUMES CRACK THE CRUST

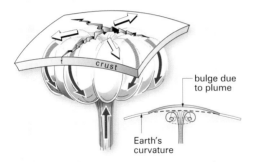

A rising hot magma plume forms a crustal bulge, which fractures along radial branches arranged at 120° to each other as Earth's gravity causes the bulge to collapse. The Red Sea, Gulf of Aden and Rift Valley may have formed in this way.

Rift valleys often contain lakes formed by the collapse of crustal slabs, which create deep depressions that later fill with water.

to the east. Examination of the seismic map of Africa suggests, however, that this is not a simple north-south split. In the far north, a single rift has developed, producing the Nubian and Somalian subplates. Just north of Lake Victoria the rift splits into two branches, which pass southwards on either side of the lake. The eastern branch exhibits limited seismic activity, but the western branch is very active. South of Lake Malawi, this branch splits again, forming a complex pattern. One branch runs southwards through Mozambique, while others extend southwestwards across Zambia. The most southerly of these passes through Lake Kariba and the Okavango Delta. The tortuous courses of rivers and the occurrence of extensive swamplands in Zambia and northern Botswana suggest that widespread tectonic movement of the Earth's surface is taking place there, disrupting river courses.

There is apparently no minimum size for continental crustal fragments, and several micro-continents are known that are generally referred to as islands, such as New Zealand and the even smaller Seychelles. If rifting persists, Africa could theoretically split further into several smaller plates, including a southern African plate and a Lake Victoria plate.

There is no doubt that rifting on the African continent is currently progressing southward. However, it is less certain how rifting will progress in the future because when rifts form at a triple junction, it is common for one of the branches to fail and rifting ceases. Considering the relative spreading rates of the three branches of the rift, it is likely that the East African Rift is actually failing and rifting may cease at some future time. If this is the case, Africa will remain intact.

AFRICA'S EARTHQUAKES

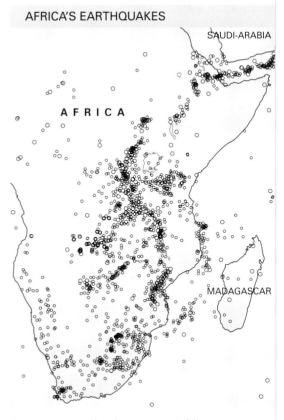

Seismic activity on the African continent delineates zones of incipient rifting.

45

HOW HAVE THE EARTH'S CONTINENTS SURVIVED PERPETUAL EROSION?

Rock exposed to the atmosphere is subjected to constant attack. Chemical reactions between rock, water and atmospheric gases cause the rock to decompose and disintegrate; this is known as weathering. Mechanical forces also break up rock. Rivers and glaciers carry objects such as sand and boulders that erode the rock surfaces they flow across, and wind has a similar but less dramatic effect. Waves too are potent agents of erosion, constantly battering shorelines around the world.

These processes convert hard rock into small particles that are transported to the oceans and deposited. Given enough time, it would seem, all land should disappear beneath the oceans, yet the world today still has many high mountain ranges. Over the past two centuries, detailed studies of rocks and rock-forming processes have revealed why the Earth is not entirely covered by water.

Rocks that form the continents are fundamentally different from those that form the ocean floors (see page 32). Ocean floors constitute about 60% of the Earth's surface area, and detailed sampling and dating of them has revealed that none of their igneous basalt rocks are older than 200 million years. Ocean floors are created by volcanic processes at mid-ocean ridges and destroyed at subduction zones. These are the key components of the conveyor system that moves continents around the globe (see page 30). Given that the Earth is about 4 600 million years old, and the ocean floor rocks are just 200 million years old, 60% of its surface has therefore been recycled in the past 5% of Earth's history.

In contrast to the ocean floors, the continents contain not only a greater variety of rock types, but also rocks of great antiquity. The oldest rock thus far discovered is a 4 100-million-year-old granite from Canada, and the oldest terrestrial object is a grain of the mineral zircon (a zirconium silicate) that is 4 400 million years old. Since continental rocks are still forming, continents preserve a much longer record of the Earth's history than do the ocean floors.

The most illuminating of the continents' diverse rock types are metamorphic rocks, which are either sedimentary or igneous and have been greatly altered by heat and pressure. From the nature and composition of distinctive minerals they contain, it is possible to determine the temperature and pressure to which they have been exposed. From such analyses we can infer that linear belts of metamorphic rocks represent the root zones of ancient mountain ranges similar to the Andes or the Himalayan range.

Several such former mountain belts occur in southern Africa. These include the 2 700-million-year-old Limpopo Belt of the Limpopo valley; the Ubendian and Kibaran Belts of KwaZulu-Natal, Northern Cape and

SOUTHERN AFRICA'S ANCIENT MOUNTAIN ROOTS

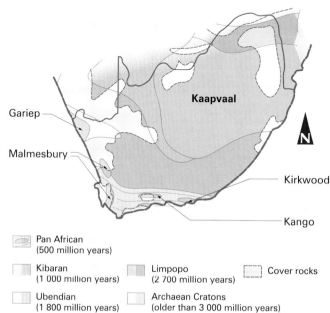

Gariep

Malmesbury

Kaapvaal

N

Kirkwood

Kango

Pan African
(500 million years)

Kibaran
(1 000 million years)

Limpopo
(2 700 million years)

Cover rocks

Ubendian
(1 800 million years)

Archaean Cratons
(older than 3 000 million years)

The linear zones or belts of metamorphic rocks in southern Africa mark the positions where huge mountain ranges once stood, formed during the collision of continents. Most of these ancient mountain ranges have been completely flattened by erosion.

Botswana, respectively 1 800 million and 1 000 million years old; and the 500-million-year-old Pan African Belts of the southern Cape and Namibia. Each of these belts of metamorphic rock once lay beneath a mountain range similar to the Himalayan range in size and stature but which has now been completely obliterated by erosion. Along the southern Cape, the Cape mountain ranges represent the last wrinkles of a once-majestic, Andean-size mountain chain formed 250 to 300 million years ago that is heading towards oblivion brought about by the relentless forces of weathering and erosion (see page 102).

Together, the record of the ocean floors and the metamorphic belts of the continents speak of a dynamic Earth. Its surface is undergoing constant change as ocean crust is recycled and continents move around, colliding with one another to form huge mountain ranges that are subsequently flattened by erosion. Eroded material is dumped in the oceans at the edges of continents that may in turn be crushed and uplifted to form new mountain ranges. Rocks tell us that these processes have been operating for more than 2 700 million years and – as seen in the Andes, the Rockies, the Alps and the Himalayan range – they are still occurring today. As fast as mountains are destroyed by erosion, new mountains form in a constant process of renewal, ensuring that the Earth is not covered entirely by oceans.

The Cape mountains are the remains of a once huge mountain range, similar to the present-day Andes. Erosion has greatly reduced their height, and will ultimately level them completely.

BIRTH AND DEATH OF A MOUNTAIN RANGE

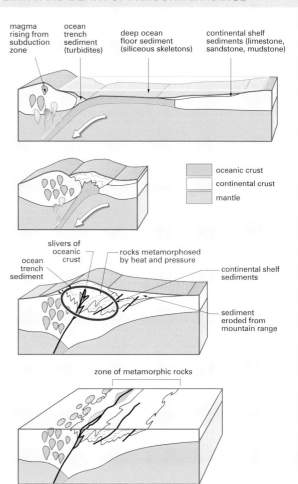

The plate tectonic process of subduction sometimes results in continental collisions (for example India and Asia). Huge mountain ranges (in this instance, the Himalayan range) form along such collision zones as the crust thickens, and the rocks in root zones beneath these ranges become metamorphosed by the high temperature and pressure. In time, erosion strips away the mountain range, exposing rocks that once formed the root zone.

COULD EARTH BE STRUCK BY A METEORITE?

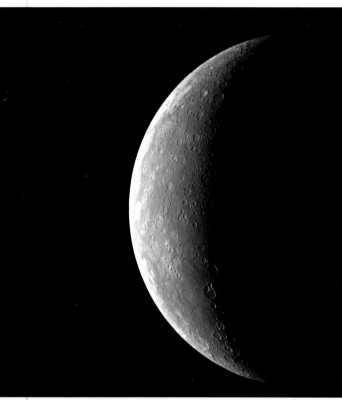

NASA / Johns Hopkins University Applied Physics Laboratory / Carnegie Institution of Washington

The surfaces of solid bodies in our solar system, such as Mercury, are pockmarked by impact craters, reflecting the important role that impacts have played in planetary evolution.

The surfaces of virtually all solid bodies in our Solar System are pockmarked by craters. First noted on the Moon, they were initially assumed to be extinct volcanoes. However, geologists in the 1950s and 60s realized that most were formed by asteroid and comet impacts.

Initially, very few impact sites were known on Earth, but once geologists became aware that impact craters abound in the Solar System, many terrestrial impact sites were discovered. Some craters previously thought to be extinct volcanoes turned out to be impact craters, such as the Tswaing crater north of Pretoria. Nevertheless, Earth has few craters because its crust is continually being reshaped by geological processes.

Impacts by bodies from space formed all the planets and even our Moon (see pages 8–11), and impacts remain a potentially important geological process on Earth. For example, their dramatic intervention in the evolution of life was revealed in 1980 when Louis Alvarez and colleagues proposed that a major impact caused the extinction of dinosaurs (see page 156). Their theory was considered interesting but esoteric until 1994, when the Shoemaker-Levy 9 comet spectacularly crashed into Jupiter and caused scars that were hundreds of times larger than Earth. Suddenly the fate of the dinosaurs raised the question of whether it could it happen to us.

So, are we likely to be blasted into extinction in the near future? Firstly we need to consider comets and asteroids as potential projectiles. Comets originate in the outer solar system far beyond Pluto, and consist mainly of ice, carbon dioxide, carbon monoxide and some rocky material. Appearing suddenly from the depths of space, most are interstellar wildcards. If on a collision course with Earth, we could have as little as six months warning, but fortunately they are rather rare. Asteroids, however, are much more common and originate mainly from the asteroid belt between Mars and Jupiter. They usually consist of rocky material, although a few are pure metal. Potentially the most threatening are the Apollo asteroids whose orbits cross that of Earth. Most of the larger kilometre-sized members have been identified and their orbits determined, and happily there is nothing on the horizon as yet! The smaller ones, however, are numerous and mostly uncharted.

Earth is constantly bombarded by material from space (about 100 tonnes per day), consisting mostly of tiny grains and dust. The likelihood of larger objects impacting Earth decreases rapidly with increasing object size. So for example, impacts by soccer ball sized objects are expected once a month, but impacts by 3 km-diameter objects are expected only once every 10 million years. The effects of an impact vary enormously with the mass and velocity of the object, normally expressed as equivalent to so many megatons of TNT explosive. The Tunguska impact of 1908 in Siberia was equivalent to 20–50 megatons of TNT, and is likely to recur every 100 years or so. This impact was probably caused by a comet, which exploded at an altitude of about 8 km

The Tswaing crater near Pretoria was formed by a meteorite impact about 200 000 years ago.

and devastated an area of about 2 000 km². Larger events such as those that created the 1 km-diameter Tswaing (Pretoria) and Barringer (Arizona) craters, for example, occur every few thousand years.

Thus, the likelihood of a moderate, Tunguska-sized impact occurring in the next 100 years is high. The Tunguska event occurred in a remote, unpopulated region, but if it occurred today over a densely populated area such as a large city in Western Europe, the death toll could reach thousands to a million or so.

Following the Shoemaker-Levy 9 event, the vulnerability of our society to an impact from space became patently obvious, so the

EARTH'S IMPACT SCARS

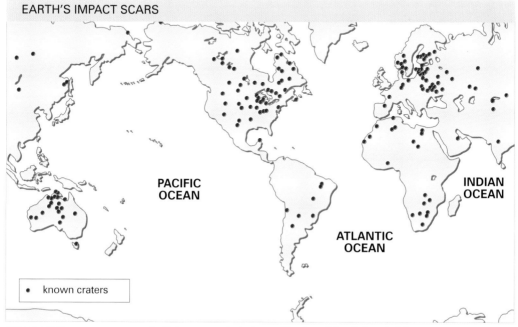

PACIFIC OCEAN

INDIAN OCEAN

ATLANTIC OCEAN

• known craters

Impact craters are uncommon on Earth because geological reworking has obliterated most of them.

US government implemented a space watch programme to identify, map and track all objects potentially threatening Earth. In 2004, just such an object was discovered. Known as Apophis, it will come within 26 000 km of Earth in 2029 – a near miss! But, unfortunately, it may get close enough for Earth's gravitational field to swing its orbit onto a collision course, resulting in an impact in April of either 2035 or 2036, or possibly later. At this stage it is uncertain if an impact will occur at all, because detailed information on the spin and solar reflectivity of Apophis are not yet properly known. But it's going to be a close call and we may only know our fate once Apophis passes Earth in 2029.

What will its impact be like? Apophis is a rocky asteroid about 260 m in diameter and weighing about 80 billion tonnes. Its estimated impact velocity is 12.6 km per second, and its impact would be equivalent to 850 megatons of TNT. The initial impact would blast a hole 1 km deep and about 2 km across, which would collapse to form a final crater 500 m deep and about 3 km across. This is about three times the diameter of the

EARTH'S IMPACT RISK

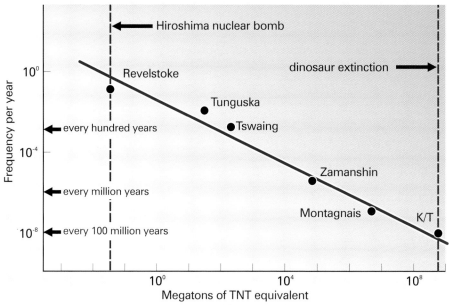

Impact severity is expressed in terms of an equivalent quantity of TNT high explosive and the risk or the likelihood per year of an impact of a given severity. Impacts by small bodies are common, but large impacts are rare.

The spectacular impacts of the Shoemaker-Levy 9 comets (seen here in transit) with Jupiter heightened public awareness of the threat posed by an asteroid or comet impact with Earth.

Tswaing crater. On impact, all buildings up to 5 km away would be flattened due to seismic shock and the air blast, and 10 m-diameter rocks would rain down. At 5–10 km away, buildings would be severely damaged and 1 m boulders would crash in. By 30 km distance, the air blast would uproot all trees and blow roofs off houses, while the seismic shock would severely crack structures, and marble-sized fragments would clatter down. Up to 80 km away, windows would blow out and some roofs would blow off. The dust cloud would extend tens of kilometres into the atmosphere and hundreds of kilometres laterally.

The financial impact could be massive, depending where it falls. Ironically, the devastation could be worse if an impact occurred in the ocean, as it would create a massive tsunami that could devastate coastlines thousands of kilometres away. But one positive aspect of any impending collision is that its time and point of impact are predictable, thus making evacuation possible and so reducing casualties.

Has anything so devastating happened recently? Apart from Tunguska, no major recent impacts have been recorded. However, volcanoes have created some spectacular blasts in the not too distant past that are comparable, based on the amount of rock displaced. Apophis might excavate a blast crater of just over 2 km^3 in volume relative to the 4 km^3 displaced by the USA's Mount St Helens volcanic eruption in 1980. Much more impressive was the 1883 eruption of Krakatoa that blew away an island of 20 km^3, creating a huge and destructive tsunami. An impact by Apophis would therefore not be the worst event of recent times.

Can steps be taken to prevent an impact? Some movie thrillers create the notion that a threatening asteroid could be blown up by a nuclear device. Both NASA and the Japanese Space Agency could probably do so, but such a blast might simply turn one impact into many, so increasing casualties and damage. A better strategy is to deflect an asteroid's course, which could be achieved by attaching rockets or even by painting part of its surface white to increase solar reflectance, provided that the asteroid is not spinning. No clear defensive solution yet exists, but NASA is planning to use Apophis as a test bed to find one, and will probably send missions to investigate the possibilities in coming years. This will be important, because future impacts are inevitable.

The 10 km-diameter Bosumtwi impact crater in Ghana hosts a large lake. The crater was formed about 1 million years ago.

3 | THE EARTH'S ATMOSPHERE AND OCEANS

HAS THE EARTH'S ATMOSPHERE ALWAYS BEEN AS IT IS NOW?

Earth's current atmosphere is 78% nitrogen (N_2), 21% oxygen (O_2), 0.9% argon (Ar) and about 0.04% carbon dioxide (CO_2). It is unusual because it contains chemically reactive and sometimes combustible gases, notably O_2 and traces of methane, that are in chemical disequilibrium. This is due to constant chemical and biological recycling. In fact, if all life vanished, O_2 would disappear from the atmosphere by reacting with organic material and with sulphur, iron and manganese in decomposing rocks. Our modern atmosphere is therefore very much a product of life, but how did its current composition evolve?

Unravelling the early composition of the atmosphere depends on chemical clues. For example, sedimentary rocks may form in contact with the atmosphere and be influenced by it. Soils are similarly influenced, while fossilized marine organisms may also preserve chemical traces of the atmosphere. By deciphering this preserved record, we can assemble the history of our atmosphere.

The oldest sedimentary rocks were deposited 600 million years after the Earth formed, so to reveal an earlier atmosphere we need to look elsewhere. Our neighbouring planets Mars and Venus have atmospheres consisting of about 96% CO_2 and 3% N_2, but no O_2, and early Earth's atmosphere was probably once similar.

Judith Kinnaird

Aquatic photosynthetic bacteria released oxygen (a waste product of photosynthesis), which oxidized dissolved ferrous iron into insoluble ferric hydroxide. Over the aeons, this precipitated as iron-rich sediment, so providing our abundant iron resources such as these at Sishen.

EARTH'S CHANGING ATMOSPHERE

The graph traces the changing composition of Earth's atmosphere over time, which evolved as a result of geological and especially biological processes.

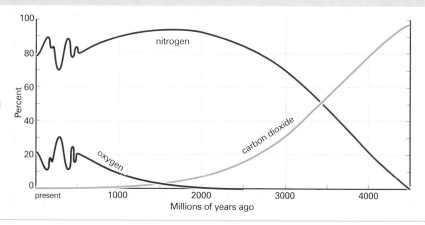

Terence McCarthy

Stromatolites, such as these found in the North West province, are rock structures formed by photosynthetic bacteria that removed carbon dioxide from the early Earth's atmosphere.

Terence McCarthy

Free atmospheric oxygen first appeared about 2 000 million years ago, manifest in red ferric iron stains in the 1 800 million-year-old sandstones of the Waterberg mountains in Limpopo province.

Bacteria are likely to have been the first life forms, arising around ocean floor hot springs about 4 400 million years ago and deriving chemical energy from vent water, much as occurs today around oceanic hydrothermal vents. The emergence of photosynthesis was a milestone, because bacteria able to synthesize organic compounds from light energy, CO_2 and water could then colonize Earth wherever there was light. The oldest evidence for this comes from 3 900 million-year-old sedimentary deposits in Greenland.

Oxygen is produced by photosynthesis, but it would be about 2 000 million years before free O_2 accumulated in the atmosphere. Nevertheless, photosynthesis probably initiated a decline in atmospheric CO_2. Carbon dioxide dissolves in water and combines with calcium to form solid calcium carbonate (limestone), a process greatly facilitated by living organisms, such as modern-day corals. While undersea hot springs and the weathering of rocks on land replenished supplies of calcium, surface-living photosynthetic bacteria strongly promoted the formation of calcium carbonate, which we see preserved in the fossil record as stromatolites – mound-like growth formed by the accumulation of calcium carbonate crystals on bacterial colonies. In this process, CO_2 was steadily removed from the atmosphere. Photosynthesis also converted CO_2 into carbohydrate, releasing O_2 at the same time. As a result, most of early Earth's CO_2 became locked up in rock as limestone, dolomite and carbonaceous material in mudstones.

Life was initially confined to oceanic surface waters, and O_2 released by photosynthesis dissolved in the ocean, which contained vast amounts of soluble ferrous iron and manganese. These elements chemically scavenged the O_2 to form insoluble red ferric iron oxide (hematite) and black manganese oxides that precipitated as sediment, so forming most of the world's iron and manganese deposits.

By about 2 000 million years ago, all ferrous iron and manganese in the oceans had been oxidized, so without a chemical demand in the ocean, free O_2 began to appear in the atmosphere. Rocks formed in contact with the atmosphere from that time bear evidence of this in the form of red iron oxide staining.

The appearance of free O_2 in the atmosphere had a profound effect on life. Oxygen was a deadly poison for most primitive single-celled species living then, so new forms of life emerged with cells containing protective nuclei and mitochondria, and in some cases chloroplasts. Their appearance laid the foundations of modern global ecosystems characterized by O_2, C and N biogeochemical cycling through the atmosphere, biosphere and rocks, and also set the scene for the evolution of more complex organisms.

As the atmosphere continued to evolve through the Precambrian Era from 4 400 to 545 million years ago, there was a steady rise in O_2 content. By 700 to 600 million years ago it had increased to about 12%, when the first multi-cellular organisms appeared and diversified, reaching a climax in the Cambrian Explosion about 530 million years ago. This laid the foundations for the variety of life we find today.

From about 500 million years ago, O_2 abundance was variable, ranging from roughly 30% 270 million years ago to 10% 190 million years ago. These fluctuations were probably the result of variable oxygenic photosynthesis due to changing global climate. For example, about 300 million years ago, huge tropical forests formed over northern hemisphere continents, increasing the atmospheric O_2 content. In contrast, when the world was hot and arid about 240 million years ago, photosynthesis was limited and atmospheric O_2 concentrations fell.

The composition of the Earth's atmosphere has therefore been a product of the dynamic interplay between life and geological processes that has operated over billions of years.

HOW VARIABLE HAS EARTH'S CLIMATE BEEN IN THE PAST?

Climate describes the average temperature, rainfall, humidity, windiness, cloudiness and seasonality of any particular region. Over time we become familiar with a region's climate and consider it normal, but of course different regions experience very diverse climate extremes. Furthermore, we know that Earth's global and regional climates have experienced dramatic changes in the past, but how variable have they been?

How is it possible to determine Earth's climate and temperature history? Past climate signatures are recorded in many geological, fossil and glacial records, as well as in some extremely long-lived plants. For example, in the oceans, microscopic surface-dwelling foraminifera build shells of calcium carbonate ($CaCO_3$) in which the isotopic composition of oxygen (O_2) varies with the temperature of the water in which they live. When they die, their shells sink to the ocean floor and become buried in the sediments, in which the deepest layers go farthest back in history. Examination of oxygen isotopes in foraminifera shells from layers within deep ocean sediment cores can therefore be used to reconstruct past ocean temperatures.

Ice cores from Greenland and Antarctica provide a long-term record of past temperatures because the isotopic composition of hydrogen and oxygen in the ice (H_2O) varies with the temperature at which the ice formed. The Vostok and Dome C cores from Antarctica provide the most continuous record, extending back about 450 000 and 800 000 years respectively. Temperatures reconstructed from both ice and ocean-floor sediment cores correspond well, giving us confidence that Antarctic ice cores provide a realistic picture of past global temperature trends. Ice cores also contain trapped gas bubbles that have been analysed to determine the past composition of the atmosphere, and especially the abundance of greenhouse gases such as carbon dioxide (see page 58). Dust present in the ice also points to periods of general aridity or large volcanic eruptions that corresponded with cooler periods.

Unfortunately the terrestrial palaeoclimate record is very sparse and imprecise. Stalagmites and stalactites in caves give indications of both temperature and rainfall based on carbon and oxygen isotopic measurements, but suitable sampling sites are quite rare and widespread. Fossil pollen in terrestrial sedimentary deposits has been used to reconstruct vegetation assemblages and these have proved to be a useful guide to past climates. In similar fashion, annual tree rings can also provide a guide to past climate over the last few centuries or so.

CORRELATION BETWEEN TEMPERATURE, GREENHOUSE GASES AND GENERAL DRYNESS (DUST CONTENT)

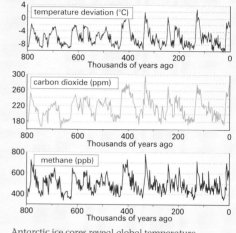

Antarctic ice cores reveal global temperature, atmospheric carbon dioxide (in parts per million) and methane concentrations (in parts per billion) over the last 800 000 years.

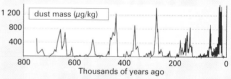

Dust concentration in the Antarctic ice increased during colder periods, reflecting drier and windier climates prevailing at those times.

Ice core records indicate that global climate has experienced substantial changes in the past million years. The mean temperature over this period was 3–4°C colder than at present, but there have been both warm and very cold episodes. The warm interglacial periods occurred approximately every 100 000 years, but generally only lasted a few thousand years. We are currently experiencing such a warm period, which commenced about 10 000 years ago. As a rule, each warm period has been preceded by an intensely cold glacial or Ice Age period that coincided with major expansion of the ice caps, especially in the Arctic. The last Ice Age reached its most intense about 18 000 years ago and it is generally believed that the interior of southern Africa was considerably drier during these cold periods (see page 114).

Studies of Antarctic and Greenland ice cores have revealed a very close relationship between temperature and atmospheric concentrations of the greenhouse gases carbon dioxide and methane. Importantly, however, it appears likely that warming preceded the rise in atmospheric carbon dioxide, indicating that the initial increase in carbon dioxide was a consequence and not a cause of temperature rise. If so, where did the carbon dioxide come from as the atmosphere warmed? About 93% of the Earth's 'active' carbon (i.e. carbon not in rock) is dissolved in the oceans, the largest and most important carbon reservoir. Of the remainder, 4.2% occurs mostly in the top metre of soils, 1.4% in biota and 1.4% in the atmosphere. In the past, small shifts in the sizes of these reservoirs caused natural fluctuations in atmospheric carbon dioxide and, therefore, temperature. During Ice Ages, the cold oceans absorbed carbon dioxide because gases are more soluble in cold water than in warm water. The reverse presumably occurred during interglacial periods, when ocean warming released carbon dioxide into the atmosphere, inducing further warming because of the greenhouse effect. This may explain rapid warming at the end of the Ice Ages. Nevertheless, the general question remains: what caused interglacial warming and glacial cooling periods if not directly the fluxes in the CO_2 reservoirs? (see page 58)

Climate over most of the past 100 000 years was so harsh that humankind was forced to eke out a living in small, nomadic hunter-gatherer communities, but during the current interglacial period from about 10 000 years ago, complex agriculture-based and

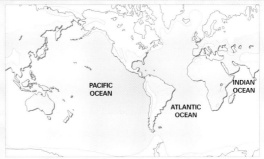

During the last glacial period, which peaked about 18 000 years ago, most of the northern hemisphere continents were buried beneath several kilometres of ice.

sedentary civilizations began to emerge around the globe as climate warmed. Not only has the present Holocene interglacial period been unusually warm, but temperature during this time has also been generally stable. An exception occurred during the Little Ice Age (1315–1860) when decades-long periods of pronounced cooling prevailed and the River Thames in London used to freeze in winter. The coldest point was reached in the winter of 1708–1709, when temperatures were 7°C below the winter average for twentieth-century Europe. Even the canals of Venice froze that year. Records from that time provide graphic insight into the consequences of global cooling. Animals and birds died in their thousands across Europe, as did hardy oak and ash trees. Soil froze to depths of up to a metre and winter crops throughout Europe failed, resulting in severe famine the following year. Another major Ice Age would clearly be catastrophic for our civilization, but set against this is the prospect of current – and rapid – global warming, with its own associated problems.

Terence McCarthy

The area where New York City now stands was scoured by glaciers as recently as 12 000 years ago, as revealed by sculpted rocky mounds in Central Park. These mounds have a gentle facing slope smoothed by the advancing ice, but a steep lee side where rock was plucked off by the retreating ice.

A. Hondius / Museum of London

During the peak of the Little Ice Age, the River Thames regularly froze over in winter, as illustrated in this 1667 painting by A. Hondius.

WHAT ARE THE CAUSES OF CLIMATE CHANGE?

The primary factor that determines Earth's climate is heat derived from the Sun, but how a particular region responds to solar heating is influenced by latitude, altitude, proximity to an ocean, ocean temperature and circulation, and local winds. We know that climate has varied in the past due to natural causes (see page 56), but there is now also concern that human activities are probably causing current rapid climate change.

The amount of solar heat that reaches Earth depends on the position of Earth relative to the Sun, as described by the three Milankovitch cycles, named after Milutin Milankovitch, the Serbian geophysicist who mathematically described them. Firstly, eccentricity describes the shape of Earth's orbit around the Sun, which varies from more or less circular to elliptical over a period of about 100 000 years. Secondly, the Earth's axis of rotation or obliquity is tilted relative to the plane of its orbit, which varies from an angle of 21.5° to 24.5° over a period of 41 000 years. Lastly, the axis of tilt slowly rotates or precesses, completing a full revolution every 23 000 years.

These cycles interact in complex ways, but when radiation is averaged over a year they account for just 0.2 watts/m² relative to the average of 240 watts received per m², thus making very little difference to the average heat budget. Much more important, however, are variations in the timing and location of radiation they cause, especially the contrast between winter and summer. The 100 000-year eccentricity cycle seems to have the most pronounced effect on global climate, and may be responsible for the warm interglacial periods (see page 56).

Although Milankovitch cycles appear to influence global climate, their effects alone are probably too small to account for climate change. Rather, it appears that certain responses in the Earth's complex climate systems amplify or moderate small variations in solar radiation. Of these, Earth's reflectivity or albedo is very important. Ice and snow reflect sunlight very strongly, reducing its heating effect, whereas deep water and vegetated areas absorb solar heat. For example, it is believed that during periods of maximum eccentricity and

EARTH'S PATH AROUND THE SUN

146 M.km 152 M.km

ellipse sun

ECCENTRICITY

variation in shape of orbit over 100 000 years

circle

21.5°–24.5°

SUN

TILT

variation over 41 000 years

SUN

PRECESSION

complete revolution over 23 000 years

24.5° warm winter cold summer 24.5°

winter SUN summer

summer winter

hot summer cold winter

MAXIMUM ECCENTRICITY, MAXIMUM TILT
(maximum summer-winter contrast)

21.5° 21.5°

winter SUN summer

summer winter

MINIMUM ECCENTRICITY, MINIMUM TILT
(minimum summer-winter contrast)

The amount of solar radiation, or heat, that reaches the Earth varies over time. It is affected by: changes in the shape of the Earth's orbit around the sun, or the eccentricity; variation in the Earth's angle of tilt; and the rotation in the Earth's axis of tilt or precession (upper diagram). These factors, known as Milankovitch cycles, interact in complex ways, and affect the contrast between the seasons (lower diagram).

Sunspots represent cooler regions on the surface of the Sun and form as a result of the development of extremely intense, localized magnetic fields. They are associated with increased activity in the Sun's interior.

tilt, a resulting succession of cool high-latitude summers would reduce winter snow melt and lead to accumulated snow cover. This would increase albedo and enhance cooling, possibly resulting in an Ice Age. A corollary is the melting of floating Antarctic and Arctic sea ice. When this ice melts, it exposes heat-absorbing water, so Earth's albedo is greatly reduced and warming is enhanced. Clouds also increase albedo but, unlike snow, they also act as thermal blankets so their overall effect on the global heat budget is relatively weak.

The slow, deeply circulating thermohaline 'ocean conveyor belt' also plays a critical role in transferring heat around the globe. In general, heat absorbed by the oceans in equatorial latitudes is transported polewards, where the absorbed heat is lost to the atmosphere. For example, the Gulf Stream carries heat from the equatorial Atlantic Ocean into the North Atlantic, and is especially important in maintaining a relatively warm western Europe. When warm, salty Gulf Stream waters reach the coast of Greenland, heat is lost to the atmosphere and the salty water cools, becoming sufficiently dense to sink into the ocean interior to form North Atlantic Deep Water at about 3 000 m, which flows southwards and helps to drive the ocean conveyor belt. However, it is speculated

THE SUN

that warming and melting of the Greenland ice cap would add fresh water to the surface of the ocean and so prevent the formation of dense saline water, thus weakening the Gulf Stream and so cooling Europe, as well as perhaps initiating an Ice Age.

Concentrations of so-called 'greenhouse gases' in the atmosphere, such as carbon dioxide and methane, are also believed to play a critical role in warming or cooling the Earth. These gases are transparent to incoming short-wave solar radiation, but as the Sun warms the Earth, some heat is re-radiated back into space as long-wave radiation. But greenhouse gases are not transparent to long-wave radiation, so the Earth's atmosphere is naturally warmed and maintained at about 33°C higher than it would be if these gases were absent. However, since the start of the Industrial Revolution in the 1750s, atmospheric carbon dioxide in the atmosphere has increased from about 280 to 380 parts per million today, largely as a result of fossil fuel combustion. This is believed to be contributing to the current rapid rise in average global temperatures. Furthermore, as oceans warm and evaporation increases, this in turn may generate

THE LINK BETWEEN TEMPERATURE AND CARBON DIOXIDE

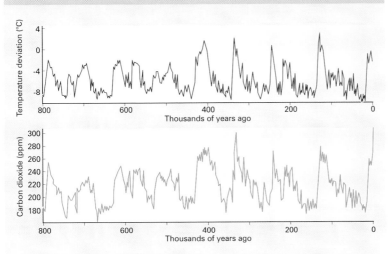

The global temperature and the concentration of carbon dioxide in the atmosphere have shown similar variations over the past 800 000 years, suggesting a link between the two.

POSSIBLE EFFECTS OF COSMIC RAYS ON GLOBAL CLIMATE

Occurrence of sunspots

Sunspots are associated with increased solar activity, including increased heat output. There were few sunspots during the Little Ice Age.

Cosmic rays and cloud cover

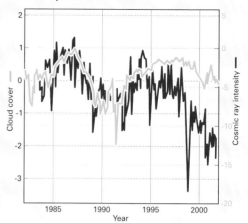

Cosmic rays may help to form clouds, which reflect sunlight and thus cool the Earth.

Solar activity and cosmic radiation

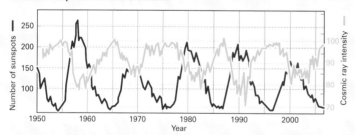

Global temperatures may be influenced by levels of solar activity. When solar activity is high, less cosmic radiation reaches the Earth.

more atmospheric water vapour and amplify the temperature rise, because water vapour is also a powerful greenhouse gas.

The Earth's largest pool of mobile carbon dioxide is in the form of dissolved inorganic carbon in the oceans. Gases are more soluble in cold water than warm water, but as water warms, gas is released into the atmosphere.

Thus where the oceans cool and sink, carbon dioxide is removed from the atmosphere, such as the 'sink' just south of Greenland, but where oceans warm, such as in equatorial 'source' regions, carbon dioxide is released to the atmosphere. Spatially and seasonally variable biological productivity of the oceans also regulates carbon dioxide concentrations through photosynthesis and respiration. The global oceans are therefore a complex mosaic of 'sources' and 'sinks' for carbon dioxide, and we are not yet certain what the net flux is, nor how this might change in the future.

Some scientists believe that variability in solar radiation also plays a part in changing climate.

Such variability is linked to the appearance of sunspots on the Sun's surface, where radiation increases with the number of sunspots. This fluctuates on a regular basis, peaking every 11 years, and has been rising steadily since the 1700s, when there were no sunspots at all. Coinciding with a particularly cold spell, this period has been dubbed the Little Ice Age. Such colder and warmer periods may reflect a 1 500-year oscillation in the intensity of solar output that could have been responsible for other major shifts in global climate over the past 10 000 years.

Cosmic radiation from deep space is another possible influence on Earth's temperature. Such radiation ionizes gases in the upper atmosphere, which promotes cloud formation and increases albedo, thus lowering temperature. The intensity of incoming cosmic radiation is affected by the Sun's magnetic field, which varies with solar activity. It is argued that during periods of low solar activity, the Sun's magnetic field is weak, and so more cosmic rays penetrate the inner Solar System, hence intensifying cosmic radiation, cloud cover and albedo, and thus cooling Earth. But as solar activity increases, the reverse occurs and Earth warms. However, the effects of cosmic radiation are small and some amplifying process is needed to cause the large oscillations in temperature observed in the past.

Global warming and the role of human activities in promoting it is a complex, controversial and emotive subject. Most scientists now believe that increasing atmospheric carbon dioxide is the primary cause of current rapid global warming, which is superimposed on natural long-term variability. However, even this view is not unanimous. While many scientists think they understand enough of the present climate system to be able to predict the effects of subtle changes in atmospheric composition, most will admit that their grasp of global climate over the longer term is far less secure. A runaway greenhouse or another Ice Age may be just around the corner, but our ability to predict either is still fraught with uncertainty.

Stephan Woodborne

The melting of floating ice sheets replaces white, heat-reflecting ice with dark, heat-absorbing water, promoting warming.

EARTH'S HEAT TRANSFER SYSTEM

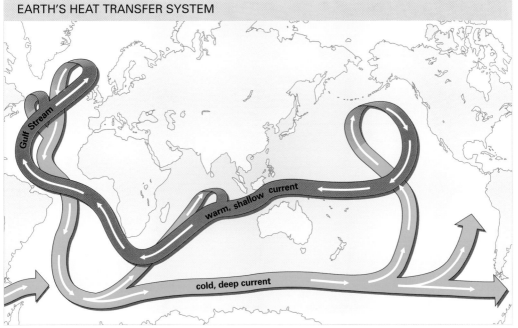

Gulf Stream

warm, shallow current

cold, deep current

Ocean circulation is important in transferring heat around the globe. The key component of this system is the formation of sea ice in the North Atlantic in winter, which drives the deep ocean circulation. If this fails, circulation will shut down and Europe and North America will freeze over.

WHAT CAUSES SEA LEVEL TO CHANGE?

Terence McCarthy

The total amount of water on Earth in its solid, liquid and vapour forms has probably been more or less constant for the past 3 billion years or so. One might therefore expect that sea level should also have been reasonably constant, but this is not the case. There have been substantial changes in sea level (by a few hundred metres) that have been caused by two very different processes.

The volume of the ocean basins that accommodate the bulk of Earth's water is constantly changing due to plate tectonic processes (see page 30). Closing of an ocean due to the convergence and collision of continents and the compression of ocean floor sediments to form high

CHANGES IN SEA LEVEL OVER THE AGES

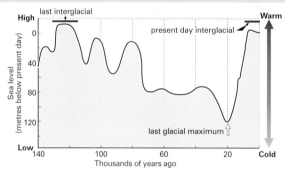

Changes in sea level on the South African coast over the past 130 000 years.

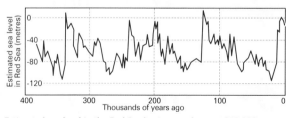

Estimated sea level in the Red Sea basin over the past 380 000 years.

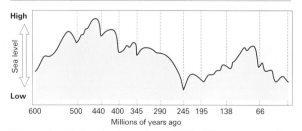

Changes in global sea level over the past 600 million years caused by changes in the volume of the ocean basins.

mountains (see page 38) effectively increases the overall volume of the ocean basins, and when this happens, sea level falls. In contrast, the extension of mid-ocean ridges, which form vast undersea mountain ranges, decreases their volume, causing sea level to rise. Changes to sea level arising from these geological processes occur gradually over tens of millions of years.

The second process governing sea level relates to changes in the amount of ice in polar regions caused by natural as well as human-induced global climate change (see page 58). Fresh-water ice sheets on land that cover Antarctica and Greenland are several kilometres thick and lock up about 90% of Earth's fresh water. Expansion of these due to further ice formation causes sea level to fall, whereas when they contract because of melting, fresh water is added to the oceans and sea level rises. Indeed, if the polar ice caps were to melt completely, sea level would rise by about 76 m! Contrary to popular belief, however, seasonal variations in the amount of floating sea ice do not affect sea level. A related effect associated with warming and melting of ice caps is thermal expansion of ocean water. Although simple in principle, the effects of thermal expansion are difficult to determine. Assuming

Beach deposits at Amanzimtoti in KwaZulu-Natal were laid down 120 000 years ago when sea level was 6 m higher than it is now.

the oceans were of uniform temperature, expansion would be about 110 mm per 1°C rise in temperature. However, ocean temperature is far from uniform, making estimates of thermal expansion difficult. Estimates of sea level rise over the last century due to thermal expansion alone vary from 30 to 50 mm.

The Earth has been cooling steadily over the past 50 million years and has been particularly cold over the past two million years. During this latter period, called the Pleistocene Epoch, the ice caps have expanded and contracted many times as the climate became alternately cooler and warmer. In periods of ice expansion during Ice Ages, most of central and northern Europe, northern Siberia, Canada and the northern states of the USA were buried under kilometres of ice. Ice ages are associated with dramatic falls in sea level, but as Ice Ages last for only a few thousand or tens of thousands of years,

the changes they cause are fairly rapid. Ice Ages over the past 800 000 years are fairly well known from the study of ice cores from Greenland and Antarctica (see page 56). The last major Ice Age peaked about 18 000 years ago and ended about 8 000 years later.

Using ice core records as well as observations and measurements made around coastlines, we can reconstruct changes in sea level in different parts of the world, including the Red Sea over the past 380 000 years and around the South African coast over the past 140 000 years. The range in sea level over the past 120 000 years has been about 130 m. Sea level was about 6 m higher 120 000 years ago than it is today, while 12 000 years ago it was about 125 m lower. Such changes have left their mark on the South African coastline and continental shelf. At Amanzimtoti in KwaZulu-Natal and at Langebaan Lagoon in the Western Cape, beach deposits formed when sea level was at its height 120 000 years ago and are now well above sea level. During periods of lower sea level, rivers eroded valleys across what is now the continental shelf, and coastal dunes formed behind the beaches, only to be submerged when sea level rose again, resulting in estuaries and undersea canyons, as well as drowned dune systems. In the Durban area, two prominent drowned dune systems have been identified. The first, some 25 m high, lies about 5 km offshore and forms Aliwal Shoal and Protea Banks. The second lies about 10 km offshore, near the edge of the continental shelf, and is about 15 m high.

Earth is currently experiencing an interglacial warm period, which began about 10 000 years ago. Consequently the ice caps are relatively small and sea level is high. The last interglacial period occurred 120 000 years ago, but at that time the climate appears to have been warmer than at present, as sea level was higher, and it is likely that Greenland had no large ice sheet covering. So, as far as we know, the current interglacial has been characterized by a relatively stable climate and hence a stable sea level.

TOPOGRAPHIC PROFILE ACROSS THE CONTINENTAL SHELF OFF DURBAN

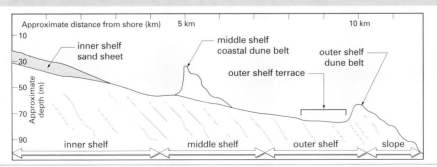

The continental shelf off Durban has two prominent drowned dune systems that formed when sea level was much lower than now.

WHAT CAUSED THE 2004 TSUNAMI?

Sunday 26 December 2004 has gone down in history as the day on which the modern world's most devastating tsunami took place. An estimated 300 000 people lost their lives as coastal villages around the northern Indian Ocean were inundated and swept away by the massive surge of ocean water.

Tsunamis are huge waves that form as a result of large-scale geological events, most commonly earthquakes, but also volcanic explosions and surface or undersea avalanches. Under certain circumstances, earthquakes cause vertical movement of the ocean floor, which acts like a piston on the water column above. The resulting disturbance is essentially a broad, large-scale ripple or wave, which spreads outward from the source at a velocity of about 700 km per hour. As the wave enters shallow water, the leading edge slows down because of bottom friction, while the trailing edge advances against it, piling water up to form a massive surge or wave that can be many metres high. The height of the surge is greatest near the source of the disturbance, but becomes smaller with distance travelled as its energy dissipates.

The 2004 tsunami originated off the west coast of Sumatra, one of the islands that make up Indonesia. The arc formed by the Andaman, Nicobar, Sumatra, Java and Timor islands forms part of the boundary between two of Earth's large tectonic plates (see page 30), these being the Australian-Indian plate in the south and the China subplate of the Eurasian plate in the north. The Australian section of the Australian-Indian plate is advancing northwards at 5.2 cm per year and is sliding beneath the China subplate, while the Indian section has collided with, and is still advancing into, the Eurasian plate.

The rate of advance is an average because the movement is generally not continuous but occurs in fits and starts. The plane along which movement occurs may 'lock' for a time, and then stress steadily mounts as the rocks bend under the compression. Eventually a rupture occurs, much like a dry twig that is being bent will suddenly snap. This releases a large amount of energy in the form of shock waves, which cause the Earth's surface to oscillate like

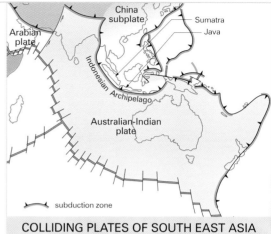

COLLIDING PLATES OF SOUTH EAST ASIA

The Indonesian Archipelago was formed by the collision of the Australian-Indian tectonic plate and the China subplate of the Eurasian plate.

ocean waves. The longer the build-up of stress, the greater the energy released. If the rupture occurs near the surface, the ground will be offset, creating a step known as a fault scarp. If such an offset occurs on the sea floor, a tsunami will be generated, as happened in 2004.

The recent history of movement along the Sumatran section of the plate boundary is quite well known. In 1833 and 1861 sudden movements occurred in adjacent sections of the Mentawai

FORMATION OF THE SUMATRAN ISLANDS

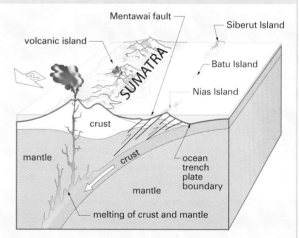

As the Australian-Indian plate moves northwards beneath the China subplate, it has formed a deep trench on the ocean floor as well as many volcanoes on islands along the plate boundary. The volcanic arc is separated from the trench by a string of islands formed as material has been pushed up by faults along the collision zone. Movement along such a fault caused the undersea earthquake in 2004.

fault between the islands of Nias and Mentawai, causing earthquakes of magnitudes greater than 8 on the Richter scale. No further movement occurred until June 2000, when slippage took place along the section of the fault extending past Enggano Island, resulting in an earthquake of magnitude 7.9.

In the 2004 earthquake, movement occurred along a 1 600-km section of the fault starting in the south near Simeulue Island and extending northwards. At a magnitude of 9.2, this was the second strongest earthquake ever recorded. Some 10 m of lateral and 4–5 m of vertical slippage occurred along the fault, displacing about 30 km^3 of sea water and creating surges estimated to have been 24 m high. The movement lasted for about 10 minutes, producing the longest earthquake duration ever recorded. The extent of the devastation caused by the tsunami probably arose from the large amount of movement on the fault and the great length of fault that experienced movement, both resulting in an exceptionally large tsunami.

The series of earthquakes between 1833 and 2004 released stress along the plate boundary from Enggano in the south to the Andaman Islands in the north, except for a short stretch between Nias and Simeulue. This section slipped on 28 March 2006, producing an earthquake of magnitude 8.6. The resulting tsunami was both smaller and more localized, with surges only 2–3 m high.

The Sumatra section of the boundary between the Australian-Indian plate and the China subplate is prone to extreme earthquakes, possibly because of the presence of irregularities in the subducting ocean floor. These take the form of swells and troughs that lie oblique to the direction of subduction, increasing the friction of the descending slab and causing an accumulation of stress that produces very strong earthquakes.

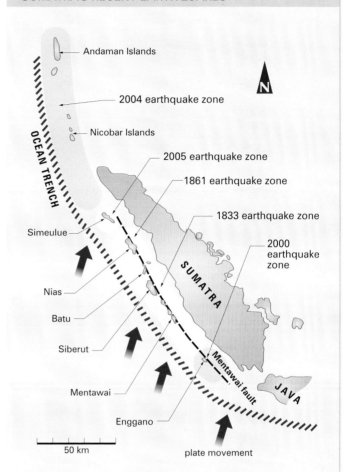

The Sumatra section of the plate boundary has experienced many severe earthquakes as a result of great frictional stress being relieved along the two plate boundaries.

Areas where tectonic plates collide are prone to earthquakes and hence tsunamis. The only escape is to reach high ground, as this sign west of Seattle, USA, advises.

65

WHY IS SEA WATER SALTY?

Sea water tastes salty because it contains a large amount of sodium chloride, known commonly as table salt. Sodium chloride is present in most fresh water, but the concentration is usually too low to give it a salty taste. In sea water, the salt concentration is just over 3% by mass, which is 3 g of salt per 100 g of water. Sea water also contains other dissolved substances, most notably calcium bicarbonate and calcium sulphate. The total dissolved solid content of sea water is therefore about 3.5% by mass and is remarkably uniform over the world's oceans.

To understand why sea water is salty, we need to examine the global hydrological and rock cycles. When the oceans are heated by the Sun, water evaporates and water vapour is transported landward by winds. As moist air rises over land it cools, the water vapour condenses to form clouds and eventually falls as rain. Some water returns to the atmosphere by evapotranspiration, while some soaks into the ground to become ground water (see page 128), and the remainder collects in rivers and flows back to the oceans. Most ground water eventually returns to the oceans either by direct subsurface flow or via rivers (see page 126). Water is therefore constantly being cycled between the oceans, the atmosphere and the land, driven primarily by heat energy from the Sun. Although the cycle is dynamic, the total amount of water in the cycle is constant and, in particular, the volume of the oceans remains essentially constant, except during Ice Ages (see page 62).

Rainwater contains no dissolved salts and is essentially distilled water, yet river water does contain dissolved substances derived from the slow dissolution and chemical weathering of rocks. The most important of these are silica, sodium, potassium, calcium, magnesium, chloride, sulphate and bicarbonate. Insoluble clays and oxides resulting from chemical weathering are transported away by flowing water as suspended silt or muddy particles, whilst soluble substances remain dissolved. In either case, both are delivered to the oceans, where particulate loads are deposited as sediments, whilst soluble ions become mixed with sea water. Sediments eventually become sedimentary rock that is ultimately recycled by plate tectonic processes, returning it to land as continental rock, thus completing the rock cycle over many millions of years.

THE WATER CYCLE

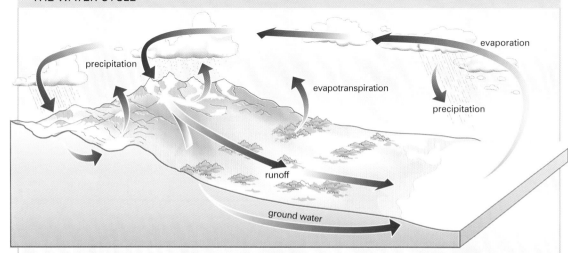

precipitation

evaporation

evapotranspiration

precipitation

runoff

ground water

The Earth's water is constantly being recycled between the oceans, the atmosphere and the land, as illustrated here.

Sea-water evaporation in shallow, restricted embayments leaves behind salt (sodium chloride), which can be commercially exploited, as at the salt works near Port Elizabeth.

Rob Duker

Rivers continually deliver dissolved substances and water to the oceans, but as the volume of the oceans is essentially constant, one might expect dissolved substances to accumulate there, perhaps eventually becoming saturated in the same way that salt pans become saturated with salt (see page 120). This is not so, however. Although rivers do continuously supply soluble substances to the oceans, salts are simultaneously being removed, so net salt fluxes are in equilibrium. How then, are salts removed?

Different substances are removed from ocean water in different ways, primarily by chemical and biological activity. For example, calcium is removed as calcium carbonate by animals and plants to construct animal bones, calcareous coral reefs, molluscan shells and the like. Similarly, silica is used to construct the delicate silicate frustules of diatoms. In all cases, the mineral elements finally become incorporated into the sediments when the organisms die and sink to the ocean floor.

In closed estuaries or shallow embayments, calcium carbonate, calcium sulphate and especially sodium chloride may precipitate as a result of evaporation. Much of our table salt is obtained in this way. Soluble salts are also removed from sea water by absorption onto electrically charged clay particles in particular, which settle onto the ocean floor.

From the ocean floor sediments, biogeochemical processes recycle some salts back into the water column, but a significant fraction nevertheless remains and accumulates in the sediments. Some elements are instead returned to the atmosphere. For example, sulphur is taken up and converted by planktonic and benthic micro-organisms into gaseous hydrogen sulphide and dimethyl sulphide that is released into the atmosphere.

Rather than steadily accumulating in the oceans, soluble ions are therefore recycled between the sediments, the sea water and the atmosphere, such that removal balances the accumulation rate. So what then determines the final concentration of dissolved salts? The more quickly a substance is removed from sea water, the less the ocean will contain, but the more slowly a substance is removed, the more abundant it will be. The rate at which a substance is removed from sea water is expressed as its residence time, which is the time a substance remains dissolved. So, for example, the residence times of sodium and chloride are extremely long at 200 and 600 million years respectively, which is why they have accumulated to such an extent in the oceans. In fact, the elemental composition of the oceans has varied very little over the past 900 million years, affirming the notion that dissolved salts in the ocean are in biogeochemical equilibrium.

Danja Kohler / IOA

Biological processes, such as the formation of shells and coral reefs by marine animals, play an important role in removing dissolved salts from sea water.

4 | THE EARTH'S MINERALS

HOW DOES URANIUM GIVE US ENERGY?

Uranium is a rare metal consisting of two major isotopes: uranium-235 (^{235}U, 0.7%) and uranium-238 (^{238}U, 99.3%). Both isotopes are the same substance, but have slightly different atomic masses. In the 1930s it was discovered that when the nucleus of ^{235}U is struck by a neutron, it becomes unstable and splits apart, emitting two neutrons. This process is called nuclear fission. As the nucleus of the uranium atom disintegrates, some of the energy holding it together is released, mainly in the form of heat.

If the two neutrons released strike other ^{235}U atoms, they induce them to disintegrate and produce more neutrons, which in turn trigger further disintegrations in a continuing chain reaction. A great amount of energy is released in a very short time, resulting in a massive explosion. This was the process behind the atomic bomb dropped on Hiroshima at the end of World War II. The runaway chain reaction can however be slowed down and halted by introducing substances that absorb the neutrons, thus preventing them from striking other ^{235}U atoms. Boron is the substance most commonly used to do this, and varying the amount allows the rate of the nuclear chain reaction and heat production to be controlled. In nuclear power stations, this heat is employed to produce the steam that drives electricity-generating turbines.

In natural uranium there are insufficient ^{235}U atoms to produce a chain reaction, so the percentage has to be increased by a process known as uranium enrichment, in which the ^{238}U atoms are separated from the ^{235}U atoms. For use in nuclear power stations, ^{235}U abundance is boosted from 0.7% to about 3%, whereas pure ^{235}U is used for nuclear bombs. Because of its high density (about 19 g per cm^3), the separated ^{238}U (called depleted uranium) has been used for military purposes, such as in armour-piercing shells.

So what is it that makes uranium potentially so dangerous, and is it hazardous where it occurs in nature? Uranium occurs naturally in chemical combination with other elements; two common forms being the minerals uraninite, also known as pitchblende, and carnotite. Uranium is an extremely rare element and because its normal abundance in rocks is less than one part per million, uranium minerals are also rare. However, under certain geological conditions, uranium may become concentrated to many hundreds of parts per million, forming deposits from which it can be economically extracted. In southern Africa there are several such occurrences. These occur associated with the gold deposits of the Witwatersrand; with calcium carbonate-rich soils (calcrete) in the more arid, western regions of the Northern Cape province and Namibia; in certain sandstones in the Karoo Supergroup strata, especially near Beaufort West; and in igneous intrusions such as that at Rössing in Namibia.

The radioactivity of uranium itself is not normally dangerous because, although a massive alpha particle is emitted in the decay process, it cannot penetrate human skin nor even a sheet of paper. If uranium is ingested, however, the radiation can cause damage to cells. In addition, the metal is chemically toxic. The radioactivity of uranium in

Guy Freemantle

Guy Freemantle

The most important minerals containing uranium are uraninite (above: small, dark grains) and carnotite (right: yellow coating).

Guy Freemantle

The Rössing uranium deposit in Namibia is the largest of southern Africa's abundant uranium resources.

rocks is a different matter however, as several of the decay products emit very penetrative beta and gamma radiation. Uranium minerals are therefore dangerous and should always be kept behind appropriate radiation shielding; usually lead. Nevertheless, the average concentration of radioactive substances in most uranium mines is not high enough to pose a health hazard, although levels of radioactivity must be constantly monitored, especially in the processing plants where uranium is extracted from the ore.

One of the intermediate decay products of ^{238}U is an isotope of the chemically inert gas radon (^{222}R), which is also radioactive. Atoms of this gas often leak from uranium minerals and can diffuse through soils and mix with the air. Radon decays by emitting an

Eskom's Koeberg nuclear power plant generates electricity using uranium and supplies it to Cape Town and surrounding areas.

alpha particle that can be dangerous if the gas is inhaled. In areas where there is a naturally high abundance of uranium, radon can pose a health hazard if it diffuses into poorly ventilated buildings.

In the nuclear fission process, the resulting fission fragments or products include isotopes of various chemical elements such as barium, krypton, strontium, caesium and tellurium. Many of these are extremely radioactive, emitting energetic gamma and beta radiation, which can pose a serious health risk.

When a nucleus of ^{238}U absorbs a neutron, it transforms into plutonium, which is thus formed in nuclear reactors. Plutonium can be used in the same way as ^{235}U both for power generation and for bomb manufacture. Pure plutonium is obtained during reprocessing of the spent fuel from nuclear reactors. Spent nuclear fuel not only contains plutonium, but also all of the fission products of ^{235}U. Spent fuel is therefore extremely dangerous and will remain so for hundreds of thousands of years. The safe disposal of spent fuel is of great concern because the material has to be contained for such a long time and no really satisfactory method has yet been found to do this.

WHY DO SOME ORGANIC MATERIALS DECAY INTO COAL AND OTHERS INTO OIL AND GAS?

Bruce Rubidge

Coal is formed from dead plant material that forms peat in swampy environments. Burial of this beneath sedimentary strata causes heating under pressure, converting the peat to coal.

Coal originates as peat, which is partly decayed plant material that has accumulated in a swamp. Peat formation, which is a very slow process, results from the incomplete decay of plant matter in wet conditions. Water shields the plants from oxygen, which would otherwise cause them to decay rapidly. Taken as a whole, peat appears to be a black and fibrous mass, but in detail its characteristics vary depending on whether it is made up of leaves or wood, and on how much decay took place before the plant material was completely submerged. Very thick accumulations of peat sometimes form under suitable geological conditions, especially where slow subsidence is taking place. When layers of peat are buried under strata of mud and sand, the pressure exerted by these overlying sediments, in conjunction with heat, gradually changes peat into coal.

Plants – and therefore peat – are made up mainly of cellulose, which consists of carbon, hydrogen and oxygen. In addition to cellulose, peat may contain mineral matter deposited from the water in which the vegetation grew. The conversion from peat to coal takes place in several stages, as pressure and heat expel hydrogen and oxygen (as water) from the cellulose, leaving behind the carbon. The first stage produces material called lignite, or brown coal, which contains about 30% carbon; next is sub-bituminous coal, containing 40% carbon; then bituminous coal, containing 50–75% carbon; and finally anthracite, which contains about 90% carbon.

Most coal in South Africa is bituminous and is usually banded. The different bands arise from the type of material that formed the peat and variations in the amount of ash present, the latter derived from mineral matter present in the original peat.

Terence McCarthy

Oil and gas are formed when muddy sediments rich in microscopic organisms become buried and heated. These may accumulate in suitably porous reservoir rocks and can be extracted by drilling wells.

The processes that produce coal also produce some methane gas, which remains trapped in the coal-bearing strata. Coal-bed methane can cause underground explosions and fires during mining, and in some areas is extracted commercially.

Oil and gas, however, form from minute single-celled plants and animals that live in oceans and lakes. These organisms die and sink, settling on the ocean floor or lakebed along with particles of mud. Where surface water biological productivity is high, the organic content of the muddy sediment is also high and can constitute several per cent of the sediment mass. For oil to form, organic-rich mud must be buried by more and more sediment and become compacted into rock and slowly heated. Various changes take place as the temperature rises, resulting in the formation of hydrocarbon compounds that contain only carbon and hydrogen. The prime source of oil and gas is believed to be the fatty compounds (lipids) found in the dead organisms. The optimum temperature for oil formation is between 100°C and 150°C (called the oil window). Below 100°C, oil will not form, while above 150°C all the material is converted to gas.

Crude oil derived from fatty compounds consists of a complex mixture of viscous materials such as tar and grease, as well as more volatile substances such as paraffin, turpentine and dissolved gases. When oil is formed at higher temperatures, there is a greater proportion of the more volatile materials. Oil may remain trapped in the source rock, resulting in an oil shale, or it may be squeezed out and collect in reservoirs of suitably porous rock. Gas may separate and form a layer above the oil in the reservoir, so both can be derived from the same well.

Conditions suitable for coal, oil and gas formation still occur today. Thick accumulations of peat are associated with tropical forests lying close to sea level, such as along the lower reaches of the Amazon and Congo rivers. Increased subsidence could result in submergence and burial of the peat beneath muddy material, initiating coal formation in these areas. Conditions suitable for the accumulation of oil precursors are taking place in regions of the ocean where upwelling of nutrient-rich water is taking place, resulting in very high biological productivity, such as off the coasts of Namibia, Chile and Peru. However, coal, oil and gas formation takes millions of years, so we will not benefit from these modern accumulations.

Robert Harding / Digital Source

Oil may sometimes be squeezed from muddy sediments and rise to the surface, where volatile constituents evaporate, leaving a tar-like residue, as at La Brea tar pits, California. Tar pits also preserve fossil remains.

Gallo Images / Getty Images

Tar sands containing viscous oils cannot be pumped, but are instead mined, crushed and heated to liberate the oil, as at Athabasca tar sands in Alberta, Canada.

WHY ARE SO MANY OIL AND GAS FIELDS LOCATED OFFSHORE?

As oil deposits on land become depleted, an increasing proportion of the world's oil is being derived from offshore deposits.

Gallo Images / Getty Images

Oil and gas form in muddy sediments rich in microscopic animal and plant remains that are compacted into rock and heated (see page 72). Because of the continuing pressure of compaction, oil migrates slowly upwards from its mud-rock source, seeking paths of least resistance. Such paths are usually found in porous rocks such as limestone, but notably in sandstones, which have water-filled spaces between their grains. Under certain conditions oil may become trapped in porous rock masses such as these, which are then termed reservoir rocks. The requirement that reservoir rocks be both porous and cooler than 100°C means that they usually lie above older source rocks.

When the single landmass Pangaea began to break up during the Jurassic Period about 200 million years ago, a network of rifts in the massive continent steadily opened and eventually flooded, becoming seaways and ultimately oceans. The Earth at that time was much warmer than it is today andmicro-organisms flourished in the rift environments, producing a steady rain of organic material onto the ocean floors. At the same time, rivers transported nutrient-bearing sediments from the surrounding land into the widening and flooded rifts, where they mixed with the organic material. From these beginnings, fertile oil source rocks were formed.

As Pangaea finally broke up and the smaller landmasses began to drift apart during the Cretaceous Period, continued erosion buried the source rocks under younger material, especially sand deposits and limestone in shallow water at the continents' edges. The now deeply buried source rocks produced oil, which migrated up into the sandstone and limestone, sometimes becoming trapped. Thus most of the world's oil and gas deposits, which originated in Jurassic rocks and accumulated in Cretaceous sediments, are found in continental shelves.

Within the past two centuries, oil has become increasingly indispensable to modern life, and as land-based oil deposits are becoming exhausted, attention is turning increasingly to offshore fields. Mineral oil and its viscous residue, tar, have been extracted from natural seeps for centuries, but man's large-scale exploitation of mineral oil is a relatively recent phenomenon, beginning in earnest only in the 1850s due to growing global industrialization. Prior to that, natural oils derived mainly from whales were used for lighting the streets of London and other cities, as well as homes. However, as whale populations declined, scientists at Dartmouth College in the United States discovered that by distilling mineral oil, they could produce kerosene, which was excellent for use in lamps. This led to drilling of the first oil well in Pennsylvania, which was completed on 27 August 1859. Thereafter, kerosene rapidly replaced whale oils for lighting.

The search for oil expanded, leading to the discovery of rich and productive fields in the western and southern states of the United States in particular. Exploration got under way in Europe too and finds

CROSS SECTION OF AN OIL RESERVOIR

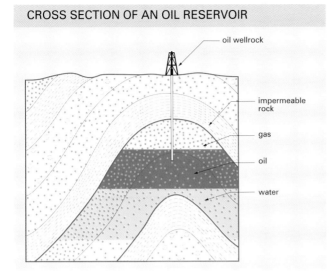

- oil wellrock
- impermeable rock
- gas
- oil
- water

Under suitable conditions oil deposits are trapped in porous rock, called a reservoir, which is overlain by a seal of impermeable cap rock. Gas typically occupies the upper reservoir, with oil beneath and water at the bottom.

in Italy in 1860 were followed by discoveries in Poland, Germany and Russia, as well as further afield in Canada, Peru, Venezuela, India, Indonesia, Japan, Trinidad, Mexico and Argentina. In 1908 the first important deposits in the Middle East were found, with further major discoveries in Iraq in 1927 and Saudi Arabia in 1938. Demand for cheap oil has increased as more and more uses for it have been found, notably in plastics. An improving technological capability to drill in deep water, combined with the immense financial resources of large oil companies, has led to oil exploration and production being extended to offshore areas. As land-based oilfields run dry, so oil production from offshore sites is steadily increasing.

Oil and gas exploration are carried out in essentially the same way, although oil is the more valuable commodity. Nevertheless, the demand for gas is increasing steadily as a replacement for coal, since it is less polluting and more energy efficient. Moreover, the development of technology to convert natural gas into more valuable liquid products has also increased the demand for gas.

THE DISTRIBUTION OF ROCKS THAT CAN POTENTIALLY HOST OIL

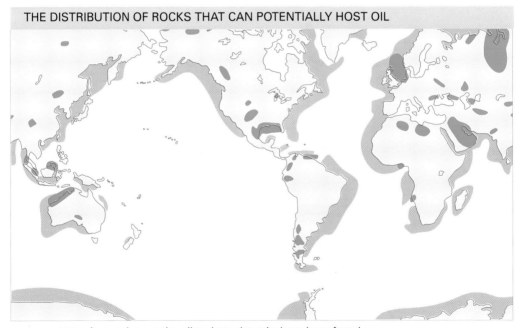

- Areas where major oil and gas deposits have been found
- Offshore areas underlain by thick sedimentary deposits

Potential oil-bearing rocks on land have been thoroughly explored and major new discoveries are unlikely. However, offshore areas offer considerable potential for new discoveries.

WHEN WILL ESSENTIAL MINERALS RUN OUT?

Many western nations are well advanced in their efforts to harness the wind as an additional source of energy and to replace our dependence on minerals for energy.

Most of the world relies heavily on mineral sources for energy, particularly coal, oil, gas and uranium. In addition, our civilization has become dependent on minerals such as iron, aluminium, tin, copper and chromium. However, we are constantly told that these mineral resources are finite and that some are running out. We know too that the time scales involved in forming new mineral deposits are measured in millions of years, set against their current rapid rate of consumption. It thus seems inevitable that we will exhaust these resources, but when?

Answering this question is, however, far from straightforward. When dealing with future mineral supply, economists distinguish between reserves and resources, in which the former are proven to exist, whilst the latter are inferred to exist, but remain unproven. Providing proof of reserves involves considerable expenditure, so mining companies generally only confirm reserves for 10 to 20 years hence. Therefore, the published reserves of any commodity invariably suggest that it will last only for a few decades before running out, which is an artificial projection. Furthermore, we usually don't know what proportion of the stated resources can be converted into reserves. Some may turn out to be smaller than expected, while others are larger, which frequently renders estimates of future resources unreliable.

Improving technology will have a major impact on the future availability of resources. For example, ever deeper offshore drilling for oil and gas has increased our access to these resources. Our ability to lay gas pipelines efficiently and cheaply almost anywhere has made gas an attractive energy resource, so its use is steadily rising. Oil and gas have therefore displaced coal as the fossil fuel energy source of choice. Copper was once widely used for high-voltage power lines, but more cost-effective aluminium is now used instead. Improvements in metal extraction technology have made mining of lower-grade ores possible. Substitution of metals by other materials has also reduced their consumption. For example, most car fenders are now made of plastic and the quantity of steel used in vehicles has declined steadily.

The life of South Africa's non-renewable energy sources could be extended by making greater use of other energy sources such as hydroelectric power.

THE PEBBLE BED REACTOR

cold helium in

fresh fuel

graphite liner

fuel and graphite pebbles

fuel and graphite pebble return line

hot helium out to turbine

fuel pebble evaluation unit

fuel pebbles are 6 cm in diameter and consist of silicon carbide-coated uranium oxide spheres embedded in graphite

spent fuel

More cost-effective ways are being sought to extend our energy supply. The Pebble Bed Modular Reactor has been proposed as one of these as it is an efficient user of uranium.

Nevertheless, as the availability of certain minerals declines, their scarcity and value will rise. Some deposits formerly regarded as uneconomic, and not currently listed as resources, will become economically viable. Deposits once abandoned because of low yields could be reopened. For example, pumping steam or solvents down disused oil wells to liberate more viscous oil residues can make them viable again. Higher prices could also make shale oil (torbanite) and tar sands economic to exploit, particularly since untapped shale oil resources are about 240 times larger than liquid oil reserves. Similar scenarios have developed with other commodities. The 1970s gold price increase made it economically viable to re-treat waste dumps from Johannesburg's gold mines, and as they still contain uranium, they will probably be recycled again in the future. Elsewhere, changes in commodity prices have made it possible to extract minerals from the sea bed, which contains potentially vast resources (see page 98).

Energy production from uranium is a particularly interesting conundrum. The present generation of nuclear reactors uses ^{235}U as fuel, but this makes up only 0.7% of natural uranium (see page 70). However, new generation Fast Breeder Reactors use the more common ^{238}U alongside ^{235}U fuel under conditions where uranium is optimally converted into plutonium, which can fuel other nuclear reactors. But there is considerable opposition to the expanded use of nuclear power, particularly that based on plutonium, however, increasing reliance on nuclear power is probably inevitable if we ever hope to stabilize atmospheric carbon dioxide concentrations. Nevertheless, the safe disposal of nuclear waste does present some problems. Research continues on harnessing nuclear fusion as an energy source, much as the Sun does (see page 10), so there could be unlimited pollution-free energy in the future.

Although Earth's mineral resources are finite, it is impossible to say when or even if we will exhaust these resources. Even so, our dependence on fossil fuels will almost certainly end in the future, but probably not because we run out. As a former Saudi Arabian oil minister, Sheik Yamani once said: 'The Stone Age came to an end not for a lack of stones, and the oil age will end, but not for lack of oil.' New technologies, substitution and recycling will probably ensure that no commodity ever limits our civilization.

Terence McCarthy

Increases in commodity prices have converted gold mine waste dumps around Johannesburg into valuable resources. Most have been recycled to extract the remaining gold, and uranium will be extracted in the future.

WHY IS SOUTH AFRICA SO RICH IN PRECIOUS METALS?

South Africa is renowned for its gold deposits, especially those of the Witwatersrand Basin, a kidney-shaped depression about 400 km long by 200 km wide. The basin is filled with layers of sedimentary rock about 7 000 m thick that were deposited between 2 970 million and 2 714 million years ago. Some of the layers are made up of conglomerate that was originally deposited as gravel and contains particles of gold.

Although not exceptionally rich in gold, as the average content in the layers mined is only about 8 g per tonne, the layers are remarkable for their continuity and their sustained gold content. Both factors have made it possible to mine the layers over many decades, and for over a century in some areas. Some 50 000 tonnes of gold have been recovered from the basin so far, representing about 30% of all the gold ever mined worldwide. An almost equal amount is known to be still present in the conglomerate layers, making the basin the largest known repository of unmined gold in the world, notwithstanding more than 120 years of continuous mining. It also boasts the largest single gold ore body on Earth, at the South Deep mine west of Johannesburg, where there is a reserve of more than 43 million ounces.

Geologists are still debating where the gold came from. Some believe in the hydrothermal theory, which postulates that it was introduced by hot fluids from an undefined source long after the rocks were deposited. Others propose 'the placer theory', claiming that the gold was concentrated in the gravel of conglomerate layers by flowing water, which can separate gold from other minerals because of gold's very high density. In this case, the gold is believed to have come from nearby source rocks that have since been eroded away. But neither theory addresses why there is so much gold in this small region compared to everywhere else on Earth.

South Africa also has the largest concentration of platinum on Earth, almost 85% of the world's known resources. Together with its 'kin' metals of palladium, rhodium, ruthenium, osmium and iridium, platinum occurs in the Bushveld Complex, a massive accumulation of igneous rocks that forms a broad, irregular basin some 600 km long, 300 km wide and 8–10 km thick. Called a complex because of the wide variety of igneous rocks present, the basin formed 2 061 million years ago. The concentration of platinum group metals in the three important platinum-rich layers – the Merensky Reef, the UG2 and the Plat Reef – is typically about 6 g per tonne, of which platinum itself makes up about one half and its related metals make up the remainder. The Merensky Reef and UG2 occur as parallel layers that lie within the broader basin of the complex (like a saucer inside a bowl), forming a smaller depression 350 km long by 150 km wide. The full extent of the Plat Reef is unknown.

Terence McCarthy

Gold from the Witwatersrand occurs in conglomerate layers, rock comprised of rounded pebbles embedded in a sandy matrix deposited in streams about 2 800 million years ago.

The process that concentrated platinum in specific layers of the Bushveld Complex is akin to the separation of oil from water, but where platinum-rich molten sulphide separated from molten silicate. Why the Bushveld Complex should contain so much platinum is less well understood. There are many similar complexes elsewhere in the world, often with sulphides, but few have the same quantity of platinum. The Great Dyke in Zimbabwe also contains high concentrations of platinum group metals and is similar in other respects, but significantly, it is somewhat older than the Bushveld Complex, having formed about 2 900 million years ago.

The reason why such a large proportion of the world's precious metals occur in a relatively small area of just 700 km long by 500 km wide in northern South Africa is still poorly understood, although some ideas do exist. When all known deposits of a particular mineral are examined in terms of their age, it appears that significant numbers of such deposits formed at certain times in the past. In the case of gold, most deposits formed either between 2 500 and 3 000 million years ago, or less than 150 million years ago. Similarly, significant platinum resources are to be found only in igneous complexes between 2 000 and 3 000 million years old, and they are absent from younger complexes. These patterns may be a consequence of changes that took place as the Earth aged. Perhaps during certain periods, its temperature and the composition of its outer layers were conducive to the formation of certain types of deposit, whereas deposits no longer formed when those circumstances changed. South Africa has an abundance of rocks dating back to when gold and platinum deposits were forming, and this may be the reason for its abundant precious metal resources.

Another possibility is that the mantle and crust beneath southern Africa were slightly more enriched in precious metals than elsewhere on Earth. Such heterogeneity could have arisen during Earth's formation, especially during the Late Bombardment that occurred about 3 900 million years ago (see page 12). Meteorites are richer in gold and platinum group metals than is the Earth's mantle and crust, so that numerous impacts by meteorites could have caused a local enrichment in precious metals.

Terence McCarthy

South Africa is the largest producer of platinum, found in narrow layers of the 8 km-thick Bushveld Complex. The most important layer is Merensky's Reef, discovered in 1924.

SOURCES OF SOUTH AFRICA'S GOLD AND PLATINUM

NAMIBIA
BOTSWANA
MOZAMBIQUE
■ Pol
R ■
■ M
J ■
W ■
B ■

N

☐ Bushveld Complex
▨ Witwatersrand Basin
⌐‾‾⌐ Kaapvaal Craton

B= Bloemfontein   M= Middelburg
J= Johannesburg   Pol= Polokwane / Pietersburg
R= Rustenburg   W= Welkom

South Africa's gold and platinum deposits lie within the Witwatersrand Basin and Bushveld Complex respectively, which occur on the Kaapvaal Craton, part of Earth's oldest continent.

WHERE DO DIAMONDS COME FROM?

Diamond is a very rare form of carbon in which all the atoms are strongly linked in a three-dimensional framework. It is consequently extremely hard and chemically inert, with a density that is relatively high (3.5 g per cm³) for an element as light as carbon.

For a diamond to form in nature, carbon-bearing material needs to be subjected to extremely high pressure, roughly equivalent to the weight exerted by a column of rock more than 100 km high, as well as considerable heat. The actual amount of pressure required depends on temperature, and as the temperature within the Earth increases with depth, physicists have been able to work out that the critical depth for diamond formation is about 150 km below the Earth's surface. Any carbon present in the Earth below this depth will be in the form of diamond, but above it, carbon will be in the form of graphite, a soft, low-density (2.2 g per cm³) material in which the atoms occur as weakly linked flakes.

Having formed deep in the Earth's mantle, diamonds are brought to the surface in a type of volcanic rock known as kimberlite (see page 82). Although in theory diamonds are unstable at the atmospheric pressure prevailing on Earth's surface, they do not change spontaneously into graphite because they need to be heated to about 700°C to do so. So, in practice, they persist almost indefinitely, as demonstrated by diamonds

Diamonds have long been highly prized for their beauty and extreme hardness, making them sought-after for both jewellery and industry.

found in the gold-bearing conglomerates of the Witwatersrand that were brought to the surface more than 3 000 million years ago. As the De Beers advertising slogan maintains, a diamond is forever.

It is possible to establish the source of carbon from which a diamond is made by examining its isotopic composition. Carbon has two main isotopes, namely ^{12}C and ^{13}C. Carbon originating from living tissue (biogenic carbon), such as coal, has slightly less ^{13}C because photosynthesis tends to favour fixation of the lighter ^{12}C atoms. Primordial carbon, however, which originates in the deep mantle, has a greater proportion of ^{13}C. Thus the origin of a carbon sample can be identified by measuring its isotopic $^{12}C:^{13}C$ ratio. The isotopic composition of diamonds in fact falls into two groups: one whose carbon is primordial (^{13}C enriched) and one whose carbon is biogenic (^{12}C enriched). Each is associated with different silicate minerals: the primordial group with olivine, in which case the diamond is known as peridotitic; and the biogenic group with garnet and a particular kind of pyroxene, where the diamond is described as eclogitic.

The association of biogenic photosynthetic carbon with eclogite is significant because eclogite is a high-pressure form of basalt, the rock that constitutes oceanic crust. It appears that eclogitic diamonds represent carbon that was originally deposited on the ocean floor by living organisms. By the process of plate tectonics (see page 30), the carbon-bearing ocean floor was subducted into the mantle and the carbon subsequently converted to diamonds, while the host basalt became eclogite. These diamonds were later conveyed to the surface by kimberlite

CONDITIONS FOR DIAMOND FORMATION

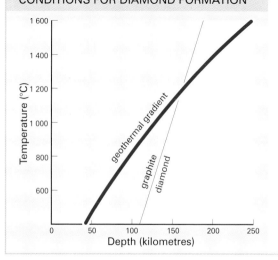

Temperature and pressure increase with depth in the Earth and cross into the region of diamond stability at 150 km depth, so natural diamonds only form and originate from below that horizon.

volcanoes. On the other hand, peridotitic diamonds represent carbon that has been trapped in the Earth since its formation.

Diamonds can also be artificially manufactured or grown. Synthetic diamonds are made by subjecting graphite to the required very high pressure and temperature in specially designed presses. Such diamonds are typically used in industrial applications for cutting and grinding hard materials. It is also possible to further 'grow' these diamonds under partial vacuum in a laboratory using a process known as Chemical Vapour Deposition (CVD). In this process, a small diamond is placed in a vacuum chamber, into which a slow stream of carbon ions is fed. These carbon ions bond to the surface of the seed diamond and replicate its atomic structure, causing it to grow in size. The longer the process continues, the larger the resulting diamond. Diamonds large enough for use in jewellery can now be made in this way, although they tend to be of lower clarity and have less desirable colours than natural diamonds. It has recently been discovered that microwave radiation can be used to improve their colour.

Although diamonds normally form at extremely high temperature and pressure deep within the Earth, it is possible to grow them in small laboratory presses, in which graphite is subjected to the necessary pressures and temperature conditions, as in this Gemesis laboratory in Florida, USA.

Rough and cut laboratory-grown diamonds.

Diamonds of a variety of colours can be grown under laboratory conditions.

WHY IS SOUTHERN AFRICA SO RICH IN DIAMONDS?

The Marsfontein kimberlite near Mokopane (Potgietersrus) is the richest kimberlite ever discovered in southern Africa, and produced 4 carats of diamonds per tonne of ore.

The first diamond discovered in South Africa was found near Hopetown on the Orange River in 1866. News of this find initiated a flurry of prospecting and further discoveries soon followed, especially along the lower Vaal River. However, the most significant finds were made in 1870 and 1871, when diamonds were located far from rivers in the kimberlite pipes that had brought diamonds to the surface from deep within the Earth (see page 80).

South Africa soon became the leading diamond producer in the world, although its standing has since waned, partly because the mines have been exhausted, but also because new discoveries have been made elsewhere. The number of carats produced by South Africa in 2005 was the highest ever up to that time, but the country ranked only fifth in the world. Add Botswana's output, however, and southern African takes the top spot. Today, diamonds are not only recovered from kimberlite pipes, but also from river gravels and beach deposits along the West Coast.

Kimberlites are typically carrot-shaped pipes of igneous rock, the solidified form of magma that once spewed out of volcanoes. Extending deep into the Earth, the pipes taper downwards, eventually becoming long, narrow and fissure-like. Diamond-bearing kimberlites have repeatedly intruded into the crust of southern Africa. The oldest occurred prior to the deposition of the 2 900 million-year-old gold-bearing Witwatersrand conglomerates, as diamonds occur together with gold in these rocks. Subsequent intrusive episodes occurred 1 600 million years ago in the Kuruman region; 1 200 million years ago near Cullinan; 560–520 million years ago in the Alldays region and extending into southern Zimbabwe; 250–200 million years ago around Jwaneng in southern Botswana and in Swaziland; and lastly, about 110 and 90 million years ago, episodes that yielded the highest number of individual intrusions, known as the Cretaceous kimberlites, and are widespread across southern Africa.

The diamond content of kimberlites is extremely variable and generally very low, with most kimberlites having no diamonds at all. The richest pipe yet found in South Africa is Marsfontein near Mokopane, which contained 4 carats of diamonds (or 0.8 g) per tonne of rock. But of the country's 850 known kimberlites, a mere 50 bear diamonds, and many of these are uneconomic to mine. Only kimberlites on the ancient cores of continents (cratons) contain the gems, apparently because the slightly cooler temperatures in mantle rock beneath these regions promote diamond stability. The Kaapvaal Craton beneath most of Botswana and northeastern South Africa and a slightly younger craton under Zimbabwe contain all the region's diamond-bearing kimberlites.

As kimberlites and surrounding rocks are eroded by water and wind (or ice in Canada and Siberia), the diamonds are released and are dispersed into rivers and ultimately into the oceans. Being slightly denser than most common minerals found in rivers, they become concentrated in river gravels and on gravel beaches, producing alluvial deposits such as those along the Vaal and Orange rivers and on the beaches of Namibia and the Northern Cape. Because they are so hard, diamonds

A KIMBERLITE PIPE AND FISSURE

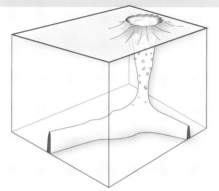

Kimberlite pipes are typically carrot-shaped, tapering downwards into narrowing fissures. Diamondiferous kimberlites originate from depths of more than 150 km, where diamonds are stable.

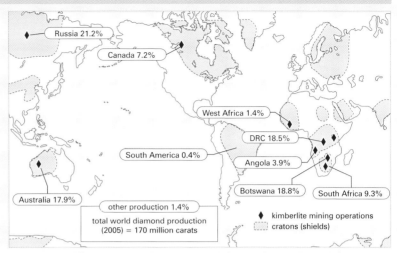

Terence McCarthy

Diamondiferous kimberlites are restricted to cratons, the ancient cores of continents dating from more than 2 500 million years ago. Cooler conditions beneath these cratons favoured diamond stability and preservation.

are also extremely durable and may be 'recycled' many times in the landscape. Some, such as those found in the conglomerates of the Witwatersrand, may have been incorporated into sedimentary deposits that were later converted into rock. When this in turn was later eroded, the diamonds were released once more and became incorporated into new gravel deposits. Thus diamonds found in sedimentary rocks today may have been borne to the surface by kimberlites billions of years ago.

So why are diamonds so abundant in southern Africa? The Kaapvaal Craton is one of the oldest on Earth and diamond-bearing kimberlites have intruded into it many times over its long history. Older kimberlites are mostly small and now hardly more than fissures because of erosion, so they contribute relatively little to total gem production. However, their diamonds have probably not been lost, but have been recycled into sedimentary rock and via re-erosion into new alluvial and beach deposits. Most diamonds are mined from younger and larger Cretaceous kimberlites that have been subjected to relatively little erosion. Although the Kaapvaal Craton is diamond rich, the Congo Craton may well be richer, but remains inadequately explored.

SOUTH AFRICA'S DIAMONDIFEROUS KIMBERLITES

1. Venetia
2. Marnitz
3. Palmietgat
4. Zebediela
5. Finsch
6. Kimberley
7. Loxtondal
8. Postmasburg
9. Barkly West
10. Premier
11. Koffiefontein
12. Theunissen
13. Jagersfontein
14. Lace and Voorspoed
15. Virginia
16. Monastery
17. Swartruggens
18. Palmietfontein
19. Dullstroom
20. Sanddrift
21. Saltpetrepan
22. Goedgevonden
23. Bellsbank
24. Boshof

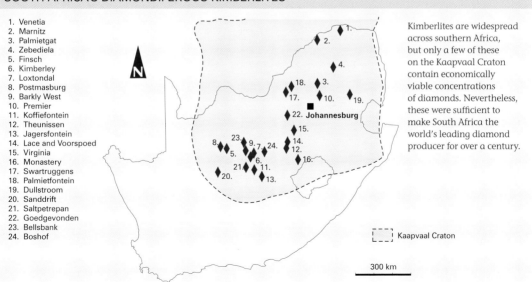

Kimberlites are widespread across southern Africa, but only a few of these on the Kaapvaal Craton contain economically viable concentrations of diamonds. Nevertheless, these were sufficient to make South Africa the world's leading diamond producer for over a century.

DO 'INTERMEDIATE' FORMS OF CARBON EXIST BETWEEN GRAPHITE AND DIAMOND?

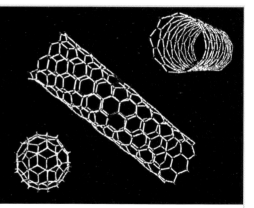

Diamonds consist of pure carbon, a remarkable substance that is unique among chemical elements in its ability to form strong bonds with itself and with other chemical elements, thereby forming complex molecules. Carbon bonds with itself in several ways, resulting in materials of different character.

In the simplest form, known as amorphous carbon and found in coal that has experienced moderate heating, the atoms are linked randomly. Under appropriate conditions, carbon atoms can link together to form small spheres called buckminsterfullerines, or buckyballs for short. These may occur naturally in soot. Another type of rare linkage creates tubular shapes.

More commonly, carbon bonds with itself under low pressure to form graphite, a stable crystalline material. Each atom is linked very strongly to three others to make a flat sheet with a hexagonal, cell-like structure like that in a beehive. Above and below each sheet is a cloud of loosely held electrons that weakly connect one sheet to another, enabling them to slide over each other very easily. Graphite is thus extremely soft, measuring 1 on the 10-point Mohs scale of

Carbon atoms can link to form spheres, called buckminsterfullerines; other types of linkage create tubular shapes.

hardness, and is widely used as a lubricant. The loosely held electrons also make graphite a good conductor of electricity. The flat nature of the sheets and their wide separation give graphite a relatively low density of 2.2 g per cm^3.

In conditions of higher pressure, the carbon sheets become kinked and link strongly together. The layers are stacked in such a way that the hexagons lie directly on top of one another, resulting in an overall hexagonal structure. This rare form of carbon, discovered in 1967, is known as lonsdaleite and has a density of 3.2 g per cm^3, reflecting the more compact arrangement of the atoms. Its hardness is not known, but could be greater than diamond, and it does not conduct electricity. Lonsdaleite occurs in certain meteorites and was found in the Tunguska crater in Russia, which was probably formed by a comet impact in 1908. This suggests that lonsdaleite forms from graphite that has been subjected to extremely high, transient pressure during meteorite or comet impacts.

Dark, hard material occurring with diamonds suggests that intermediate forms between graphite and diamond may exist. In fact, these are aggregates of microscopic diamond crystals, often mixed with other minerals. Carbonado (left) is a variety of micro-diamond aggregate of extra-terrestrial origin. A pure natural diamond is shown on the right.

De Beers Group Exploration / Ingrid Chinn

De Beers Group Exploration / Ingrid Chinn

More common than lonsdaleite, diamond is the better-known high-pressure form of carbon. As in lonsdaleite, the hexagonal sheets are kinked, but their vertical arrangement is different, where each successive sheet is displaced by half a hexagon so that the overall structure has a cubic form. As the strong links between the carbon atoms occur in three dimensions, diamond is extremely hard, registering 10 on the Mohs scale. The compact arrangement of atoms also gives it a relatively high density of 3.5 g per cm³, and like lonsdaleite, it does not conduct electricity.

Apart from coal, graphite and diamond, do intermediate carbon forms occur? The answer is no, although diamond mines often unearth strange carbon forms, some of which may *appear* to be intermediate between diamond and graphite. These usually range in colour from grey to black but are hard and dense. Occasionally they occur with diamond, as do so-called 'hailstone diamonds' that have concentric layers of clear diamond separated by dark layers without crystal form.

Dark, irregular materials associated with diamonds are in fact microcrystalline carbon forms. Ballas, which are found in kimberlites, are spherical bodies formed by the radial growth of microcrystalline diamond from a common centre. Also found in kimberlite is framesite, an irregular polycrystalline form of diamond. Inclusions of other minerals usually give polycrystalline forms a dark colour. Carbonado is a dark form of diamond found in alluvial deposits in Brazil and the Democratic Republic of Congo, and contains small metallic inclusions that are unknown on Earth. It appears likely that carbonado is of extraterrestrial origin and came to Earth aboard meteorites or comets. Carbon is a common element in clouds of extraterrestrial dust, and it seems that microcrystalline diamonds may form in these clouds, possibly in supernova explosions or perhaps by a process akin to chemical vapour deposition (see page 80).

So, while carbon does exist in a number of different forms, each with its own unique atomic structure, there are nevertheless no intermediate forms between graphite and diamond.

THE ATOMIC STRUCTURE OF THE MAIN FORMS OF CARBON

SIDE VIEW

TOP VIEW

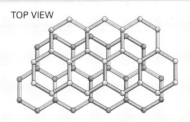

Graphite is a common form of carbon in which the atoms are linked to form sheet-like hexagonal arrays. The sheets are weakly linked together, making graphite very soft.

SIDE VIEW

TOP VIEW

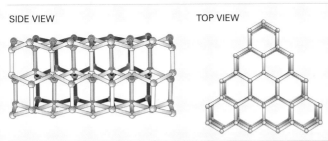

Lonsdaleite is a rare form of carbon in which hexagonal sheets are strongly linked together, and may form when graphite is subjected to transient high pressure.

SIDE VIEW

TOP VIEW

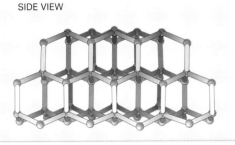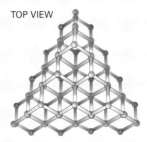

Diamond is the common high-pressure form of carbon. Hexagonal sheets of carbon atoms are strongly linked, as in lonsdaleite, but offset from each other.

WHAT IS THE ORIGIN OF SOUTH AFRICA'S WEST COAST DIAMONDS?

Kimberlite arises from deep within the Earth's mantle and is the ultimate source rock of diamonds.

Bruce Cairncross

Diamonds in southern Africa occur in three different types of deposit. These are kimberlite pipes, alluvial deposits related to present or ancient rivers, and beach deposits along the west coast of South Africa and Namibia. The primary source of diamonds is kimberlite pipes on the Kaapvaal Craton, which intruded on several occasions since the craton formed more than 3 000 million years ago (see page 82). The youngest of these intrusions occurred in the Cretaceous Period between about 110 and 90 million years ago, and most of the region's diamonds come from these rocks.

Kimberlite erodes relatively easily and in the process its diamonds disperse, finding their way into streams and rivers and ultimately into the oceans. Being chemically inert as well as hard and resistant to abrasion, diamonds survive transport by rivers and the grinding action on gravel beaches. They are also denser than most common minerals, so flowing water tends to concentrate them by washing away less dense material, resulting in the formation of diamond deposits in river and beach gravels. Diamond-bearing gravel may become buried and converted into sedimentary rock, as happened for example when the conglomerates of the Witwatersrand goldfields formed about 2 900 million years ago. When exposed at the surface, conglomerates such as these are eroded, releasing their diamonds to become reincorporated into new generations of river or beach gravel.

In light of the above, the occurrence of diamonds along southern Africa's west coast seems straightforward. Diamonds were eroded from kimberlites in the interior and transported by rivers to the coast, where they were deposited. Some diamonds were retained in river gravels along the way, accounting for the inland alluvial diamond deposits. But on closer examination, however, this explanation has some serious flaws.

Only the Orange-Vaal river system could have carried diamonds to the coast, as it is the only system that extends onto the craton where diamondiferous kimberlites occur. The Benguela Current flows along the west coast from south to north, so diamonds transported by the Orange River should only occur north of the river mouth. However, diamonds are found all along the west coast to as far south as the Olifants River. How did they get there?

Furthermore, diamond-bearing gravels occur along the Vaal River and the Orange River as far as Prieska, and then again downstream from Vioolsdrift, near the Orange River mouth. But few occur between Prieska and

DIAMOND DEPOSITS OF SOUTHERN AFRICA

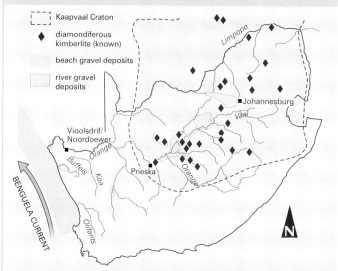

Legend:
- ⬚ Kaapvaal Craton
- ◆ diamondiferous kimberlite (known)
- beach gravel deposits
- river gravel deposits

Labels: Limpopo, Johannesburg, Vaal, Vioolsdrif/Noordoewer, Orange, Buffels, Koa, Prieska, Orange, BENGUELA CURRENT, Olifants, N

Southern African diamonds are extracted from kimberlite pipes and fissures, river gravels, and beach deposits. The ultimate source of the diamonds is the kimberlite pipes of the Kaapvaal Craton.

Viooldrift. Had the Orange River been the major carrier of diamonds from the craton to the coast, gravels along its entire length should contain the gems. What caused this gap? Finally, diamonds have been found in gravels along west-coast rivers such as the Buffels and the now-defunct Koa River, whose sources lie far from the Kaapvaal Craton. Where did these diamonds come from?

One theory proposes that the Orange River once flowed into the Atlantic via the Olifants River, later changing its course in two stages; firstly following the Koa River, and then along its present route. This explains the distribution of diamonds along the coast and in the Koa River, but does not adequately account for the absence of alluvial diamonds between Prieska and Viooldrift. It also fails to explain the presence of diamonds in the Buffels and other west-coast rivers.

A modified version of this theory suggests there were once two major west-coast rivers. The Kalahari River drained southern Namibia but carried no diamonds and discharged at the present-day Orange River mouth. The Karoo River drained the interior, including the Kaapvaal Craton, and discharged at the mouth of the Olifants River. Subsequently however, the Kalahari captured the Karoo River to form today's Orange River. This theory proposes that the Koa River diamonds were derived by erosion of the alluvial deposits of the lower Karoo River, which accounts for diamonds along the coast, but not for the gap between Prieska and Viooldrift, and nor the presence of diamonds in west-coast rivers.

A third hypothesis suggests that diamonds released by the erosion of kimberlites on the Kaapvaal Craton have not yet passed beyond Prieska and are still located in alluvial deposits in the interior. Coastal diamonds therefore derive instead from other sources, particularly from glacial deposits of the Dwyka Group of sedimentary rocks (see page 110). This theory proposes that older generations of kimberlite on the craton, as well as associated alluvial diamonds, were eroded by ice and spread westward into today's Northern and Western Cape. Erosion of glacial deposits by numerous coastal rivers, such as the Buffels and Olifants, dispersed these diamonds along the west coast, where they became concentrated by wave action in beach gravels. This theory explains the presence of diamonds along the coast, in coastal rivers and in the Koa River, and accounts for their paucity between Prieska and Viooldrift. But a critical question remains. Could the Dwyka rocks have contained sufficient diamonds to produce the west coast's rich deposits, given the apparent relative scarcity of pre-Cretaceous kimberlites on the Kaapvaal Craton? We will only learn the answer when we find a way to distinguish between diamonds from kimberlites of different ages.

THEORIES ON THE EVOLUTION OF THE ORANGE RIVER

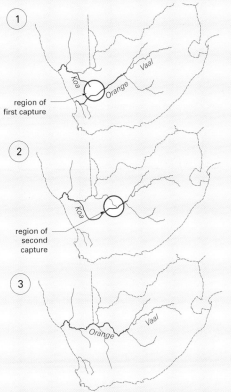

Coastal diamonds may have been delivered by the Orange River, which formerly discharged via the present-day Olifants River, before later changing its course.

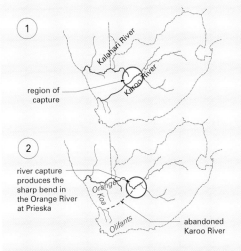

Another theory proposes that ancient Kalahari and Karoo river systems once drained southern Namibia and the diamondiferous interior, but later combined as the Orange River system.

HOW DO GOLD NUGGETS FORM?

Gold nuggets are lumps of gold, usually with roughly rounded surfaces, that can weigh as little as a gram or, in exceptional cases, as much as 70 kg, such as the 'Welcome Stranger' nugget, found in Victoria, Australia, in 1869. They are found in soils (termed eluvial deposits) or in river gravels (alluvial deposits) and normally in places where there is primary gold mineralization in the bedrock.

Many primary gold deposits form underground in cracks (veins) when gold metal precipitates from hot water as it rises and cools.

These are known as hydrothermal gold deposits and they typically occur in volcanic regions. They are still forming today, especially around the Pacific Rim. In general, the concentration of gold in the precipitating solution is very low and the precipitated precious metal is finely disseminated, but occasionally large lumps of gold do form.

Gold-bearing veins usually form an interconnecting network, which may extend underground to depths of many hundreds or even thousands of metres. Quartz, or silicon dioxide, is invariably associated with the gold and forms the bulk of the material in the veins, together with various metal sulphide minerals, notably iron sulphide. This is known as fool's gold because it looks deceptively similar to the real thing. When a vein system is subjected to weathering and erosion, the gold is released and disperses into the soil (eluvial gold), and is gradually carried downhill by soil creep into streams. It is in such streams that prospectors search for traces of (alluvial) gold, hoping to be able to follow them back to the vein source, known as the 'mother lode'.

Any lumps of gold in a vein also become detached as a result of weathering and as they pass through soil and into streams, their rough edges become rounded. The nuggets thus formed usually contain traces of their primary origin in the form of silver and inclusions of quartz or other primary minerals. Their silver content is often relatively high, amounting to several per cent, but is still lower than in the pure primary ore, as some silver leaches out of the nugget or is removed by a slow process of oxidation.

There are many recorded instances of nuggets in which the gold is quite different in composition from the gold in veins in the underlying bedrock. In such cases, notably in Australian goldfields, gold nuggets invariably have a high

Bruce Cairncross

Gold is sometimes precipitated, along with white quartz (silicon dioxide), in cracks in rocks when hot water circulates underground. Normally, such gold is finely disseminated, but occasionally large lumps form.

Bruce Cairncross

Gold precipitated in veins can occasionally occur as crystals, such as this extremely rare octahedral gold crystal.

purity in excess of 95%, with silver making up the rest. The nuggets may sometimes also contain lumps of iron oxide and bauxite, both of which are minerals characteristic of soils.

Gold nuggets of this kind are believed to have formed in the soil, although the exact mechanisms are not fully understood. It is thought that finely divided gold present in primary sulphide minerals is released when the minerals oxidize on exposure to air. The gold may be rendered soluble by humic acids or other organic compounds present in the soil, or by sulphur-oxygen compounds formed by the oxidation of sulphides. The dissolved gold is then carried away by groundwater and may be later precipitated by organic matter or by bacterial breakdown of substances that rendered the gold soluble.

The composition of the precipitated gold seems to be related to the composition of the groundwater. Alkaline, oxidizing water produces gold with 2–6% silver, whereas more acidic, reducing conditions result in pure gold precipitates. The gold itself may provide a nucleus on which additional groundwater-borne gold can precipitate, producing larger nuggets. As the gold precipitates, soil

particles such as iron oxide and bauxite may be incorporated within it. Lumps of gold evidently form relatively rarely, however. More commonly, gold precipitated in soil takes the form of wire-like threads, gold films, sponge gold or small octahedral gold crystals.

Gold nuggets (above and below) are typically lumps of gold with more or less rounded surfaces caused by tumbling during transport in streams.

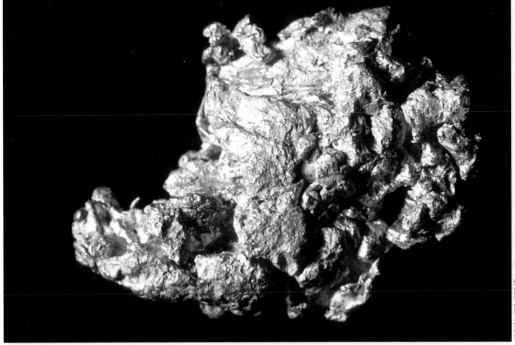

89

ARE MINERAL DEPOSITS FORMING TODAY?

Natural processes sometimes cause large quantities of a metal or mineral to become concentrated in one place, and usually in these deposits the metals are hundreds or thousands of times more concentrated than is normally found. In the South African platinum and chromium deposits, for example, the concentration of platinum is about 400 times greater than the average abundance of this metal in the Earth's crust, while that of chromium is about 3 000 times above normal. The processes that give rise to mineral deposits are very varied. Some occurred at specific times in the Earth's history and will not happen again, whereas others can be ongoing.

The world's large iron and manganese deposits formed when bacteria appeared around hot springs on the ocean floor about 4 400 million years ago (see page 54). Their photosynthetic activity produced oxygen, which oxidized the huge amounts of soluble ferrous iron into its insoluble ferric form, which then precipitated and was incorporated into the sediments. Manganese precipitation occurred in similar vein. In due course all the soluble reserves were exhausted and no further precipitation occurred, so the formation of these large deposits ceased and will not be repeated.

Deposits of iron and manganese are still forming however, since free oxygen in the atmosphere causes reduced forms of these metals to oxidize and then precipitate from any water-based solution in which they occur. Iron deposits, in the form of bog iron ore, occur at certain springs where iron-rich groundwater emerges at the surface and comes into contact with oxygen. Because of its low solubility in an oxygen-rich environment, iron can also become concentrated in soils, where it appears as iron laterite. Both types of deposit were mined by Iron-Age people, but now they are considered too small to be mined economically. Manganese deposits form by oxidation during the weathering of dolomite, and in South Africa they have been mined near Zeerust in North West province and at Randfontein, Gauteng, but again the deposits are very small. Vast iron and manganese deposits also continue to form on the deep ocean floor at the sediment-water interface (see page 98).

The formation of chromium deposits in large igneous intrusions such as South Africa's Bushveld Complex appears to have involved the Earth's ancient mantle, and mineral deposits of this type do not occur in similar rocks of younger age. The reason for this is uncertain, but it may relate to cooling of the mantle, where molten rock that gave rise to the Bushveld Complex and similar igneous intrusions originated. Such deposits will probably not form again.

Tony Camacho / IOA

Gold is actively precipitating in hot spring systems in volcanic areas around the Pacific Ocean, such as in North Island, New Zealand.

Concentrations of copper, lead and zinc formed at hot springs on the ocean floors in the past and continue to do so today. Such deposits have been mined on land for centuries, and in the future are likely to be exploited on the ocean floors (see page 98). Much of the world's titanium is mined from beach deposits, where dense minerals containing the metal continue to be driven ashore by the action of waves and wind. The supply of bauxite, and hence aluminium, is also continuously being replenished by prolonged weathering and leaching of tropical soils where bauxite occurs.

Although certain types of deposit are still forming, the minerals concerned cannot be regarded as renewable resources because their rate of formation is so slow (over thousands to millions of years) relative to the rate at which we consume these resources.

Bauxite, the principal source of aluminium, continues to form in the highly leached soils of tropical rainforests.

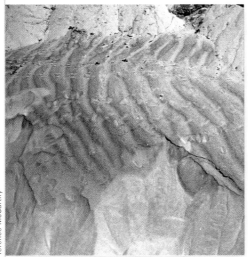

Titanium and other metals are extracted from sand dunes along the KwaZulu-Natal and Western Cape coastlines. The metals occur as oxide minerals that become concentrated by wind, which blows less dense minerals away, but leaves dense, metaliferous minerals behind. Oxide minerals commonly cause blackening of beach sands.

Coal deposits form from peat, the partially decayed organic material deposited in swamps. Peat deposits are still forming in various locations, but conversion to coal requires burial beneath layers of rock and prolonged heating, and takes millions of years.

WHAT GIVES GEMSTONES THEIR COLOUR?

Colour is probably the most striking feature of precious and semiprecious gemstones, and it serves to distinguish one type of gemstone from another. But what is it that makes a ruby red, an emerald green and a sapphire blue?

The colour of a substance arises from the interaction of light with the atomic structure of that substance. White light, such as sunlight, is actually a mixture or spectrum of light of many different wavelengths or colours. This can be seen as sunlight passes through a glass prism or droplets of rain, when the light spectrum is separated to produce the rainbow spectrum of red, orange, yellow, green, blue, indigo and violet.

White light falling on a substance may either entirely or partly pass through it, be reflected, or be absorbed. The colour of reflected light depends on the relative transmission, absorption and reflective properties of the substance. For example, when natural light passes through a glass window, transmission is very nearly 100% and the window is therefore transparent. However, if all the light is reflected in a coherent way, the substance behaves like a mirror. Alternatively, if the light is scattered, the substance appears white (like a cloud), but if all the light is absorbed, the substance appears black. Between these extremes lies the realm of colour, when parts of the light spectrum are absorbed, reflected or transmitted. The colour we perceive depends on which colours of the light spectrum have been removed.

The most common cause for the absorption of specific spectral colours is the presence of certain light-absorbing chemical elements in the crystal structure of the substance; notably titanium, vanadium, chromium, manganese, iron, cobalt, nickel and copper. The colour or spectrum of light absorbed by any one of these elements varies, depending on the nature of the host substance. In minerals, the absorbing element may be an integral and essential component of the mineral, or it may be present in trace amounts as an impurity. Gemstones are the crystalline forms of minerals, and any colour they have will depend on the absorbing element in the specific gemstone.

The semiprecious gemstone peridote, which is the crystalline form of olivine, is olive green in colour due to the presence of the essential constituent iron, which absorbs red and violet light. The mineral corundum (aluminium oxide) is white or colourless in its pure form, but trace amounts of chromium in place of aluminium atoms in the crystal structure make corundum red, which we call ruby. Chromium absorbs yellow to violet light while the red portion of the spectrum is transmitted. In contrast, trace amounts of chromium turn the normally colourless mineral beryl a deep green, creating the form of beryl commonly called emerald. Beryl and corundum are normally white or colourless when pure, and in both cases the colour is caused by impurities. Chromium absorbs differently in these minerals because of differences in their crystal structures.

The exchange of electrons between adjacent atoms of different charge in the crystal structure (known as charge transfer transitions) can be induced by incident light, causing absorption of certain wavelengths. For example, the transfer of

ABSORPTION OF LIGHT BY RUBY AND EMERALD

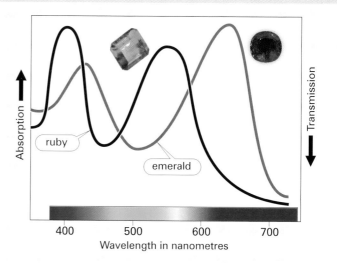

Chromium impurities in rubies absorb violet and yellow light, causing them to appear red, but traces of chromium in emeralds absorb orange and violet light, making them appear green.

Fluorite (calcium fluoride) is normally colourless, but when crystals grow rapidly, structural defects occur that trap light-absorbing electrons, making the mineral purple.

Quartz (silicon dioxide) is colourless when pure, but it can be found in virtually any colour due to various light-absorbing impurities as illustrated by these five examples of quartz.

electrons between reduced ferrous iron (Fe^{2+}) and oxidized ferric iron (Fe^{3+}) causes the blue colour of aquamarine, a variety of the mineral beryl. In another example, the electron transitions between titanium (Ti^{4+}) and Fe^{2+} iron in the mineral corundum impart the blue colour of sapphires. The normally colourless mineral quartz (silicon dioxide) can occur in a variety of colours due to electron exchange involving impurities. Iron atoms (replacing silicon atoms in the structure) produce yellow (citrine) or purple (amethyst) colours, while traces of aluminium result in a dark brown colour (smoky quartz).

Spectral absorption can also be caused by defects in crystal structure. During the rapid growth of fluorite (calcium fluoride) crystals, fluorine ions may be omitted from the atomic structure and their place occupied by roving electrons. These electrons absorb light at specific wavelengths, resulting in the blue to purple colours often seen in this mineral.

It is also possible to change the colours of some minerals by exposing them to ionizing radiation or heat treatment. Ionizing radiation can dislodge ions in a crystal structure, resulting in roving electrons that absorb light at discrete wavelengths and thus cause the substance to become coloured. Sodium fluoride and sodium chloride turn purple and yellow, respectively, when exposed to powerful x-rays, while diamonds turn green on exposure to gamma rays or radioactive sources that emit neutrons or electrons. The colour will intensify with increasing exposure.

In substances that acquire their colour from charge transfer, applying heat can also transform the colour. High temperature slightly alters the position of the atoms around the absorbing ions, changing the wavelength at which they absorb light. Thus, when amethyst (purple) is heated it becomes citrine (yellow).

HOW DO AMETHYSTS FORM INSIDE A GEODE?

From the outside, a geode is a nondescript and drab-looking more or less spherical lump of rock. But inside it is hollow and often sparkles with a spectacular lining of purple amethyst crystals. How do they get there?

Geodes come in two forms. One occurs in volcanic rock and the other in fine-grained sedimentary rock. The best-known volcanic form is found in the Paraná lavas at Rio Grande do Sul in Brazil, where the geodes are lined with large amethysts, a purple variety of quartz (see page 92), as well as some calcite crystals. Similar but less impressive geodes occur in lavas in the Jozini area of KwaZulu-Natal.

At the great depths where volcanic lava originates, the high pressure enables gases such as carbon dioxide and water to dissolve in the molten rock. When the lava erupts at the surface, the gas comes out of solution, forming bubbles like those in a carbonated drink. As the molten rock cools and solidifies, it traps the bubbles in the rock. Usually the cavities are small, but occasionally they can grow to the size of a football or larger, as they do in Paraná.

These geodes have a thin outer lining of microcrystalline quartz (agate) and an inner lining comprising six-sided pyramidal crystals of colourless quartz, which grade upwards to the purple amethyst variety. Studies suggest that negative pressure developed in the gas cavities

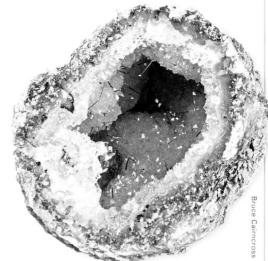

The drab outer surface of the geode starkly contrasts with the spectacular interior.

as they cooled, thus creating a vacuum, which drew in geothermal water containing dissolved substances, especially quartz and calcium carbonate. The agate linings appear to have formed soon after water began to fill the cavities, whereas the larger quartz crystals developed later, during a period of slow cooling, over a temperature range from about 240 to 100°C.

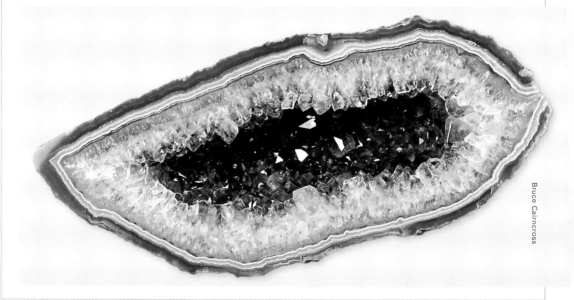

As the crystals grew, additional solutes diffused into the cavities from the surrounding rock and crystallization continued. Changes in the composition of the solutes over time resulted in variations in the colour of the quartz crystals, with an increase in the iron content giving rise to the purple of the Paraná amethysts. It appears that falling temperatures may have halted the crystallization process before the cavities were completely filled, so the cores are hollow.

Geodes in sedimentary rock formed when spheres of calcite – or sometimes gypsum – were replaced by other minerals, especially quartz. Known as concretions, the spheres themselves formed before the sediment was converted into rock, crystallizing from material in the water that filled the spaces between the sediment grains. Later, as the chemical environment in the sediment altered due to changes in temperature and pressure, the original concretions were replaced from the outside by new chemicals, commonly quartz, almost molecule for molecule, but often leaving a core of the original crystalline material. Subsequently, when the rock was exposed by erosion, the more soluble core dissolved, leaving a hollow quartz sphere with an inner lining of crystals.

Former gas bubbles trapped in the Paraná lavas (above and below) in Brazil are often lined with spectacular amethyst crystals.

Geodes often have an outer layer of agate (above and opposite) with an overgrowth of coloured crystals that line the interior cavity.

HOW DO AGATES FORM?

Agates are nodules of quartz (silicon dioxide) that show banding, which is usually concentric, and they are often coloured. Usually found in rocks of volcanic origin, they tend to occupy cavities that formed as bubbles of gas became trapped in solidifying lava, but they may also occur in crack-like openings. The banding may be uniform across the agate or fine at the edge, becoming coarser towards the middle, sometimes culminating in a crystal-lined cavity in the centre (known as a geode, see page 94). Alternatively, the outer portion may be concentrically layered, with the inner central core having linear parallel layers, which would have been horizontal when the agate formed.

Bruce Cairncross

Agates are lumps of quartz that show internal banding. They are usually coloured, most commonly in shades of red to brown, although other colours do occur.

The internal structure of agates consists of microcrystalline fibres of quartz that are often twisted and mixed with an unusual form of silicon dioxide called moganite. The crystal size of the microcrystalline quartz varies from tiny (micron) to larger (millimetre) crystals in a repetitive manner, producing the banding characteristic of agates. The colour in agates is most commonly caused by the presence of iron oxides, which occur either as a very finely dispersed dusting or as small spherical bodies among the fibres. Occasionally bands of non-crystalline silicon dioxide occur, which are usually white. Agates can be coloured artificially by introducing dyes into the layers, which differ slightly in their porosity. The internal structure of agates is more or less the same, irrespective of their age; and to the naked eye a 3 000 million-year-old sample looks much the same as one that is 10 million years old. From this we can deduce that the processes that form agates have remained unchanged for billions of years. There may, however, be subtle variations relating to age. In older agates, the grain size seems to become slightly coarser and the quantity of moganite decreases. While the internal structure of agates is well known, their origins remain a mystery. They occupy former gas bubbles in lava, and seem to have formed after the lava solidified. But even this is uncertain, as one theory for their

Terence McCarthy

Agates sometimes show concentric outer banding, and linear, parallel banding in the centre. The inner bands would have been horizontal at the time the agate formed.

origin proposes that they developed from silica-rich globules in the molten lava, rather like oil droplets dispersed in water. Another theory suggests that agates formed from a silica gel introduced by hot water flowing through recently solidified lava flows, since hot springs in volcanic areas are rich in silica. It is believed that the gel crystallized concentrically, starting from the outside in a series of pulses, initially involving rapid crystal growth that produced very small crystals. Later, as crystal growth gradually slowed down, the crystals became larger and then stopped growing for a while, until the next pulse. Pulsing could result from the build-up of heat released as the quartz crystallized (latent heat), which would then slow and eventually stop crystallization. Cooling would then occur, leading to super-saturation in the fluid and another pulse of crystallization would commence. Most of the gel is believed to have crystallized on the walls of the cavity, but a residual watery fluid may have formed tiny crystals that settled under gravity to produce horizontally layered agate.

However, none of these theories adequately accounts for all the features observed in agates, and it is still not known where the original silica comes from or how it is deposited, or when and at what temperature agate formation occurs.

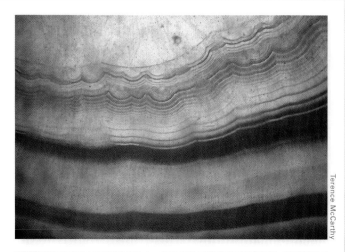

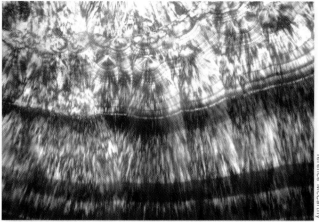

The colour in agates is usually caused by the presence of minute particles of coloured minerals, usually iron oxides. These microscope photographs of the same area of an agate were taken using ordinary light (top) and polarized light (above), and demonstrate how polarized light reveals the complex, fibrous structure of the quartz.

GRAIN-SIZE CHANGES IN AGATE LAYERS

growth direction

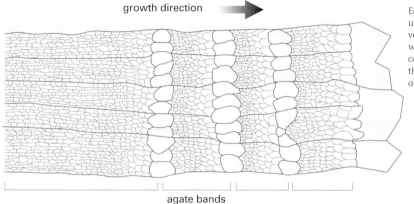

Each agate layer usually starts with very fine quartz which becomes coarser and then terminates abruptly.

agate bands

COULD MINERALS ON THE SEA BED EVER BE MINED?

We know that exploitable reserves of oil and gas occur on the sea bed (see page 74), but what about other minerals? Geologically there are two different kinds of sea bed. Deep-ocean abyssal plains are underlain by basalt, a dense igneous rock, whereas shallow continental shelves lie on less dense granite (see pages 30–33). Sedimentary deposits cover both kinds of sea bed, and can become quite thick on or near continental shelves. It is in such deposits that oil and gas are sometimes found.

Continental shelves are also the location of so-called 'placer' deposits, or concentrations of dense minerals. Rivers, wave action and wind readily transport particles that are smaller and less dense, while those that are larger and denser are more difficult to transport and so become concentrated in one place. Minerals concentrated in this way are denser than average, chemically inert and robust enough to avoid being worn away by constant abrasion. Around southern Africa, certain beaches contain rich deposits of diamonds, which are mined along the western shore of South Africa and Namibia, while sand dunes containing zirconium and titanium minerals are exploited at Namaqua Sands on the west coast, and at Richards Bay on the east coast. Similar deposits also occur below sea level in ancient beach deposits and dunes that formed when sea levels were lower than today (see page 62).

Among other kinds of mineral deposits found on the sea bed, the most extensive are potato-sized nodules containing high concentrations of phosphates or manganese oxide. Phosphate nodules are generally found on continental shelves, where they are formed by the chemical precipitation of phosphate at the sediment-water interface. Manganese nodules, on the other hand, usually occur at the bottom of deep oceans, particularly the central Pacific and Indian oceans. These nodules typically contain about 25% manganese, 15% iron, up to 2% each of nickel and copper as well as high concentrations of cobalt. They are believed to have formed as a result of undersea hot-spring activity as well as from chemical changes that occur at the sediment-water interface on the ocean floor. Metal resources contained in these nodules are vast.

Undersea hot springs associated with volcanic activity are responsible for another type of mineral deposit that is widespread on abyssal plains at depths greater than 2 000 m. Cold water drawn down into cracks in the ocean floor around undersea volcanoes, especially along the mid-ocean ridges, is heated by the surrounding rock and leaches out various metals as well as sulphur. This water then emerges at hot springs on the ocean floor, cools rapidly and precipitates its metals in the form of metal sulphides. Another type of metal deposit forms from metal-rich brines released when sediment on the ocean floor becomes compacted and loses its residual water. Brine pools accumulate in depressions on the sea floor, from which zinc and copper can precipitate as sulphides.

So we know that mineral deposits occur on ocean floors, but is it possible to mine them? The notion may seem far-fetched, but in fact we have been taking minerals from the sea bed for decades. Perhaps the most common commodities we extract are sand and gravel used in building. The technology to do this was adapted from dredgers that clear sediment from harbour entrances by means of various bucket excavator systems, and has been used to extract gold from the sea bed in Alaska and tin from the coasts of Thailand and Indonesia.

Certain continental shelves are littered with nodules rich in phosphorus. It is planned to mine these off the coast of Namibia. Nodules rich in manganese, which also contain cobalt, nickel and copper, litter the deep ocean floors, and one day will also be mined.

John Rogers

Other technology has also been used. In the late 1950s, a Texan, Sam Collins, pioneered the use of submersible vacuum pumps to extract diamond-bearing gravels from the sea bed off Namibia.

Modern technology has transformed offshore mining, especially for diamonds, and today a significant proportion of southern Africa's coastal diamond production comes from the sea bed. Old pump systems have largely been replaced by 250-tonne robotic mining tools, which excavate diamond-bearing material from depths of up to 200 m and transfer it to a parent ship, where the gems are extracted. As mineral resources become increasingly scarce on land and commodity prices rise, even deep metal sulphide deposits containing gold, copper, zinc and silver are being targeted, with exploration under way off the coasts of New Zealand and Papua New Guinea, and around Micronesia (a Pacific island state to the north of Papua New Guinea). Undersea phosphate deposits are also being sized up for mining, especially off the coasts of Namibia and Peru. It is therefore increasingly likely that a considerable proportion of our future mineral requirements will be met from mining undersea deposits.

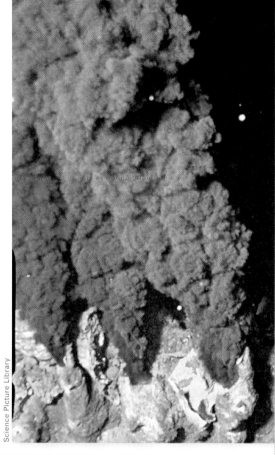

Science Picture Library

Right: Hot springs on the ocean floor discharge water rich in metals, which precipitate as the water cools forming dark clouds (called 'black smokers'). This material settles on the sea floor, forming metal-rich layers. As all of the world's oceans were formed at mid-ocean ridges, it is likely that metal deposits of this type are widespread.

De Beers / Marine and Mineral Projects

Sea-floor mining technology is becoming increasingly sophisticated, and the latest generation of undersea machines used to mine diamonds consists of 250-tonne robotic leviathans, such as this one manufactured by Marine and Mineral Projects, Cape Town.

5 THE WORLD AROUND US

WHY IS TABLE MOUNTAIN FLAT?

Shaen Adey / IOA

This question is interesting in itself but even more so when one considers that Table Mountain is composed of the same rocks and was subjected to the same disruptive forces as the Cape Fold Mountain ranges that extend from the Cedarberg southwards to the Hex River and eastwards to include the Langeberg, Swartberg, Outeniqua and Suurberg.

The rocks that make up these mountains were deposited between 500 million and 330 million years ago when the configuration of the world's continents was very different from today. Southern Africa formed part of the Gondwanan supercontinent (see page 30), and the region that is now occupied by the Cape Mountains lay beneath the shallow Agulhas Sea.

Deposition of sediment in this sea formed three groups of sedimentary rocks that make up what is today known as the 'Cape Supergroup'. Sand deposited in a near-shore marine environment gave rise to the sandstones of the Table Mountain Group; mud deposited in deeper water gave rise to the Bokkeveld Group mudstones; and sand deposited in riverine deltas and shallow marine settings formed the Witteberg Group sandstones. All of these rocks contain fossils of the marine animals living at that time – evidence of their submarine origins. Their total thickness amounts to about 10 000 m.

Most of the Cape Supergroup lies on even older and very intensely folded sedimentary rock (known variously as the Malmesbury, Kango and Gamtoos Groups of rocks). These substrate rocks had been crushed and heated during the assembly of this portion of Gondwana about 550 million years ago.

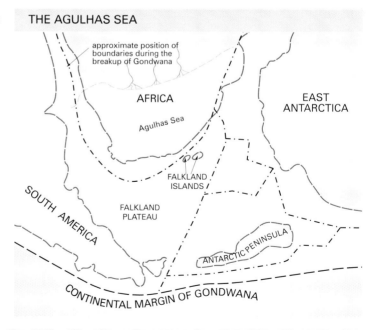

THE AGULHAS SEA

approximate position of boundaries during the breakup of Gondwana

AFRICA

Agulhas Sea

EAST ANTARCTICA

FALKLAND ISLANDS

SOUTH AMERICA

FALKLAND PLATEAU

ANTARCTIC PENINSULA

CONTINENTAL MARGIN OF GONDWANA

Rocks of the Cape Supergroup were deposited in the Agulhas Sea between 330 and 500 million years ago.

During this event, great blobs of molten rock injected into the folded sedimentary strata, where they slowly solidified, forming the crystalline Cape Granites.

In the period from 280 to 240 million years ago, the region that included the Agulhas Sea experienced compression: the sedimentary deposits of the Cape Supergroup became folded and emerged from the sea to form a mountain range (much like the Alps). Folding was particularly pronounced where the Cape Supergroup lay on older folded rocks as they offered little resistance to the compressive forces. In contrast, the crystalline Cape Granite behaved as a rigid block and resisted compression. Hence Cape Supergroup strata lying on a floor of granite, such as on the Cape Peninsula and in the Stellenbosch area, were protected during the compression and were not folded, while all around them the identical strata lying on older sedimentary rocks became buckled and folded, forming the Cape Fold Mountains.

The rocks of the Cape Supergroup contain hard and soft layers (sandstones and mudstones respectively) and the softer layers erode preferentially. Where the layers have been folded, erosion of the softer layers results in very rugged topography such as can be seen in

Rocks of the Cape Supergroup became folded due to intense compression, as seen here in the rugged terrain around Meiringspoort.

the Cape Fold Mountains. Where the layers escaped folding and are still in their original horizontal attitude, harder layers tend to protect underlying, softer layers. Consequently, erosion proceeds in a more orderly fashion, producing generally less rugged terrain. Erosion of soft layers often leaves hard layers to form flat-topped mountains and hills. Erosion of underlying softer layers results in undermining of the harder layers and they collapse to form near-vertical cliffs. Thus Table Mountain, which consists mainly of horizontal sandstone layers, has a flat top and is surrounded by steep cliffs.

WHAT CAUSES HOT SPRINGS?

Iceland, New Zealand's North Island and Yellowstone National Park (USA) conjure up images of steaming hot springs. These occur in regions of active volcanic activity, or, as at Yellowstone, where a massive underground chamber filled with molten rock boils underground water to produce spectacular geysers. Most underground water comes from rainwater or snow melt that seeps into fractures and other openings in the ground, where it may come into contact with hot rocks and become heated. In South Africa, there are no active volcanoes or recent intrusions of molten rock. The most recent volcanic activity occurred 40 million years ago in the Northern Cape, so there is no molten rock available to heat groundwater. But we nevertheless have hot springs, so how are these heated?

In South Africa, a hot spring is defined as one of 25°C or more, which applies to about 90 hot springs in the country. The hottest is Brandvlei near Worcester (Western Cape) at just over 60°C , followed by Tshipise in Limpopo at 58°C. Brandvlei also has the strongest flow, yielding about 11 000 m³ per day. The majority of springs occur in the higher-rainfall regions of the southern and eastern parts of the country, while hot springs are rare in the more arid western regions.

All South Africa's hot springs originate from very deeply circulating groundwater, which originally fell as rainfall. Heating is due to the temperature of deep underground rock, which here increases at between 15°C and 25°C per km depth (see page 18). This means that by 2 km depth, rock temperatures can reach 70°C. Under normal conditions, water does not emerge from such depths, but at the majority of hot springs in South Africa, deeply penetrating fractures or faults allow water both to reach those great depths and return to the surface, heated. However, conditions required to achieve this must be just right. A suitable collection area must exist where rainfall seeping into the ground can be directed into a fault and later emerge as a hot spring below the elevation of the collection area. Flow restrictions must exist at shallower levels between the spring and the collecting area so that water is forced to the surface from great depths. Not surprisingly, however, these conditions are infrequently met, so most springs emerge only from shallow depths and are therefore unheated.

All spring water contains substances dissolved from rocks through which the water passes; usually sodium, potassium, calcium

Terence McCarthy

In volcanic areas, hot springs abound, such as at Yellowstone National Park, USA. There are no volcanoes in South Africa, and local hot springs are due to other causes.

and magnesium bicarbonates, chlorides and sulphates. Solute concentration varies widely in our hot springs, with the most saline containing about 2.5 g of dissolved solid per litre. The relative proportions of solutes also vary widely depending on rock types and the duration and volume of water that was in contact with the rocks. Spring water often also contains dissolved gases, such as trace amounts of hydrogen sulphide, which gives the water a rotten egg smell. However, the most abundant gas is nitrogen derived from air dissolved in rainfall. Oxygen is also captured in this way, but is lost under ground due to various chemical oxidation reactions. Methane can also be included if groundwater passes through rocks containing coal. Trace amounts of argon may be acquired from the radioactive decay of potassium, while helium may be included from the radioactive decay of uranium and thorium. The highest helium concentration (10 % by volume) comes from a hot spring near Piet Retief. Solutes may sometimes precipitate as spring water emerges, forming a spring mound. At the hot springs at Warmwaterberg and Caledon in the Western Cape, iron and manganese compounds have precipitated to form large mounds, while the Florisbad hot spring near Bloemfontein has a spring mound composed of calcium carbonate. A steady year-round supply of water may also promote plant growth and the formation of peat spring mounds.

SOUTH AFRICA'S HOT SPRINGS

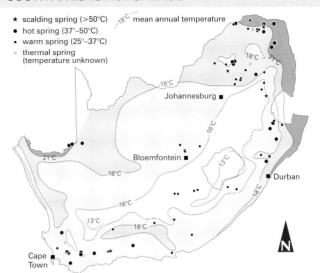

★ scalding spring (>50°C)
● hot spring (37°–50°C)
• warm spring (25°–37°C)
○ thermal spring (temperature unknown)
18°C mean annual temperature

Hot springs occur mostly in the southern and eastern parts of the country where rainfall is higher.

GEOLOGICAL CROSS SECTIONS OF SOUTH AFRICA'S HOT SPRINGS

Buffelshoek warm spring — collection area
fractures
increasing temperature
impermeable sandstone
granite basement
fault zone
permeable contact zone

impermeable shale
Die Bad hot springs
collection area
increasing temperature
weakly permeable sandstone
impermeable slate

All of South Africa's hot springs are formed by the deep circulation of groundwater under very specific geological conditions, such as at Buffelshoek in Limpopo and Die Bad in the Western Cape.

We can measure how long ago spring water fell as rain by using radiometric carbon 14 (^{14}C) dating techniques. Carbon dioxide dissolved in groundwater is usually derived from decaying organic material in the soil through which the water has passed, so its (minute) ^{14}C content is the same as that of living matter. Once water penetrates below the soil, no further ^{14}C is added, so it decays at a known but very slow rate. The water's age is therefore determined by measuring how much ^{14}C is left in the spring water. Relatively few age determinations have been made on hot-spring water in South Africa, and ages vary widely. Spring water emerging at Brandvlei, Goudini and Die Bad (Western Cape) is only a few decades old, while that at Montagu, Caledon and Malmesbury (Western Cape) is several thousands of years old. However, hot-spring waters at Warmbaths (Limpopo) fell as rain between 17 000 and 19 000 years ago, reflecting the immensely slow rate at which the water circulates through the rock fractures.

WHAT IS PUMICE AND WHY IS IT FOUND ON LOCAL BEACHES?

Pumice is volcanic foam and consequently full of tiny bubbles. It floats on water, and in this way can drift across the seas to far-off shores.

Terence McCarthy

Terence McCarthy

Pumice is a gas-bubble-filled volcanic rock of such low density that it floats on water. Put simply, pumice is solidified volcanic foam in which the gas bubbles are surrounded by a thin film of gas-tight volcanic glass, similar to window glass. Because of its unique properties, pumice is widely used as a lightweight building material and is also used as an abrasive that is especially good for removing skin calluses.

A bottle of carbonated soft drink provides a convenient way to illustrate how pumice forms. Such drinks contain dissolved carbon dioxide under pressure, but when the bottle is opened, the internal pressure is released and the dissolved gas comes out of solution as a stream of bubbles. But when the bottle contents are disturbed before opening, such as if the bottle is shaken, the gas comes out of solution all at once, turning the drink instantly into froth that squirts out of the bottle. By analogy, molten rock (or magma) can behave in a similar way.

Magma exists tens of kilometres below the Earth's surface under enormous pressure and contains dissolved steam as well as several gases including carbon dioxide, sulphur dioxide and argon. If magma rises towards the surface, the gases form bubbles, which separate from the magma as it rises. Rapid rise leads to expansion of the gas-magma mixture, which can cause it to fountain from a volcanic vent. If the pressure on the magma is released suddenly, however, many small bubbles form instantly and explosively, resulting in pumice. Sudden pressure releases occur when gas pressure builds up in a volcano, causing the volcano to blow off its top. Pressure on the magma below the mountain is then released and huge quantities of pumice are rapidly formed, causing a massive explosion. Such eruptions can be extremely violent and can produce huge quantities of pumice, amounting to several cubic kilometres. For example, the Krakatoa explosion

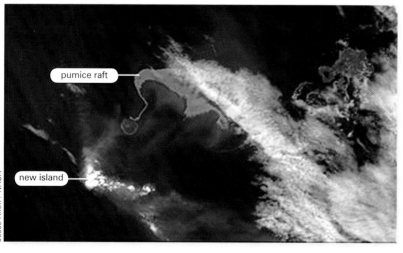

A pumice raft in the Tonga Islands as seen on a LANDSAT image in November 2006.

pumice raft

new island

Jesse Allen / NASA

of 1883 in Indonesia blew away 25 km³ of mountain, much in the form of pumice.

Volcanoes likely to produce pumice often occur near oceans in volcanic island chains or are undersea volcanoes. Because it floats on water, the sea surrounding such an eruption site becomes covered with pumice fragments, which have sometimes been encountered by passing ships. In 1725, the vessel Lyell came across pumice floating over an area of about 480 by 80 km some 800 km east of Tristan da Cunha, probably originating from an undersea eruption. In 1962, the Royal Navy ship HMS *Protector* came across floating pumice over an area of 80 by 35 km near the South Sandwich Islands that probably originated from an undersea eruption just a few weeks previously. In that area, pumice was concentrated into streams by wind. Fragments were only a few millimetres in diameter at the edges of the area, but increased in the centre to over 40 cm in diameter. The huge Krakatoa eruption of 1883 left vast areas of the Sunda Straits covered in rafts of pumice, which took ships days to crunch their way through. A massive

Most pumice found on South Africa's beaches comes from the 1883 Krakatoa eruption. A secondary source is the South Atlantic, while a few fragments originate from Tonga in the Pacific.

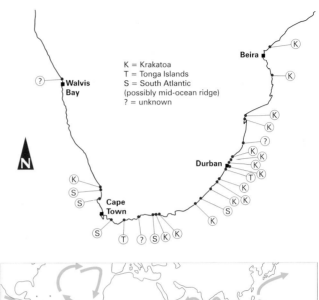

Pumice is widely dispersed by ocean currents, and fragments from eruptions in Tonga have travelled halfway around the world to reach our shores.

pumice raft was observed by yachtsman and by satellite in November 2006 around the Tonga Islands.

Pumice is easily and very widely dispersed by winds and ocean currents, which is why we sometimes find it on our beaches. Finding the source of pumice is not that simple, however, although chemical fingerprinting can provide some clues. Magma from a particular eruption generally has a fairly characteristic chemical composition, so chemical analyses of pumice samples will identify those that come from the same source. But quite where that source lies is more difficult to determine, unless there are samples of pumice from known sources to compare with. Some assistance is provided by the fact that pumice has a relatively limited lifetime because it is relatively soft and easily abraded on beaches. It probably also slowly reacts with sea water, eventually losing its buoyancy and sinking. Thus the life of pumice fragments in the ocean is probably only about a century or two, so any pumice on our beaches must have come from relatively recent eruptions.

On our beaches, pumice fragments of up to 10 cm generally occur along the highest spring tide storm mark, washed ashore by various ocean currents. A raised beach containing pumice fragments has been identified near Cape Columbine in the Western Cape, representing some ancient eruption. Pumice samples commonly found on the southern African coast between Port Elizabeth and Beira are believed to come from the 1883 Krakatoa eruption. Less common are fragments of unknown age found mainly along the Western Cape coast, which might possibly come from a long-ago eruption somewhere along the South Atlantic mid-ocean ridge. Other samples studied are believed to have come from a 1963 eruption in the Tonga Trench.

HOW HAS THE KAROO CHANGED OVER TIME?

The Karoo is a semi-arid geographic region lying in the southern part of South Africa. It is generally quite hot, and vegetation is sparse. Rocky outcrops are common, and frequently show obvious horizontal layering. There are two components to the Karoo region, consisting of the Little Karoo lying between the Langeberg-Outeniqua and Swartberg mountain ranges, and the Great Karoo to the north of the Swartberg. The Great Karoo region is underlain by the very extensive Karoo Supergroup of rocks deposited between about 300 and 200 million years ago, under conditions very different from those existing today.

The Karoo Supergroup rocks were deposited when South Africa formed part – and lay near the southern margin of – Gondwana, then located near the South Pole (see page 110). This continental boundary was similar to the present eastern margin of the Pacific Ocean and was rimmed by a mountain range resembling the Andes, because of the presence of a major subduction zone (see page 30). High mountain ranges such as these depress the Earth's crust, leaving a depression or basin on the inland side in which eroded sediment accumulates. Being near the South Pole, our region of Gondwana was under ice, and there was insufficient sediment to fill the basin, so it filled with water instead, forming a vast lake. Glaciers flowed off the mountain range and 'calved' (broke up) into the lake, where they melted, depositing glacial debris (see page 110). The lake was deep along its southern margin, but shallowed to the north where glaciers were grounded, so glacial deposits were thinner. The lake was probably connected to the open ocean by narrow inlets, perhaps similar to the Black Sea, and the water was brackish or saline, but there were apparently no tides.

As Gondwana moved northwards into more temperate regions, glacial ice cover decreased and eventually disappeared altogether, replaced by large river deltas and extensive swamp forests on the northern margin of the lake. These swamp forests gave rise first to extensive peat deposits that progressed to coal deposits with burial, becoming known as the Ecca Group of the Karoo Supergroup. In the south, along the coastline that bordered the mountain range, deltas were much smaller because of the more rapid increase in water depth, and there were no extensive swamp forests or subsequent coal deposits. Instead, the high mountains eroded rapidly and vast quantities of sediment were shed into the lake from the south, gradually filling it up. Rivers transporting this sediment now meandered across huge floodplains and discharged into the rapidly shrinking lake, forming sedimentary deposits known as the Beaufort Group.

Continued northward migration of Gondwana transported the region into equatorial latitudes and arid climates where inflowing rivers became more ephemeral, so the lake fragmented into salt pans, and sand dunes began to appear. As the climate became even drier, a vast sea of sand formed. The sediments deposited at this time are known as the Stormberg Group.

Finally, about 180 million years ago, the break-up of Gondwana commenced. As the continent began to split, vast quantities of molten rock poured through the cracks, covering the landscape beneath with layer upon layer of lava to a final thickness of about 1 600 m. But not all the molten

ROCKS OF THE KAROO SUPERGROUP

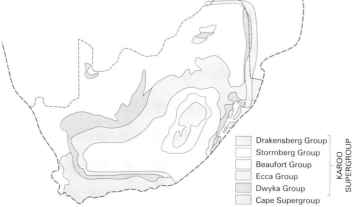

Drakensberg Group
Stormberg Group
Beaufort Group   KAROO SUPERGROUP
Ecca Group
Dwyka Group
Cape Supergroup

The Karoo Supergroup of rocks takes its name from the Karoo geographic region, but the rock group extends throughout South Africa.

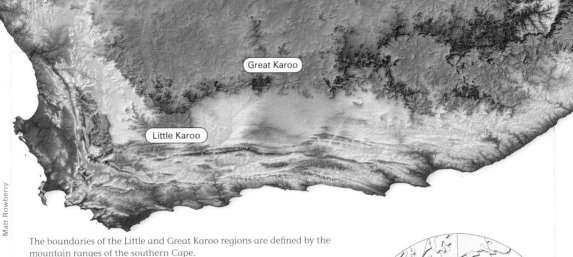

The boundaries of the Little and Great Karoo regions are defined by the mountain ranges of the southern Cape.

rock reached the surface. Some forced its way between layers of sedimentary material to form sills, while some solidified in cracks to form dolerite dykes. As the fragmentation of Gondwana followed, the Indian Ocean and then the Atlantic opened. Rivers eroded back from these new coastlines, exposing the layered deposits of the Karoo Supergroup. In the Northern Cape, North West and Limpopo provinces, the Karoo rocks have been completely removed by erosion, exposing the older underlying rocks, whereas in KwaZulu-Natal and Lesotho, the complete rock pile is still locally present. Thus, a road trip from Cape Town to central Lesotho would take you from the underlying basement rocks through the entire 12 000 m-thick pile of horizontally layered deposits.

It is thus evident that the modern Karoo is completely unrelated to the Karoo of 300 million years ago when the Karoo Supergroup formed under conditions very different from today.

Southern Africa lay close to the margin of Gondwana during deposition of the Karoo Supergroup strata.

HOW THE KAROO HAS CHANGED OVER TIME

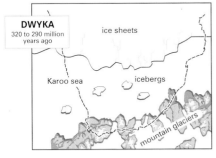

DWYKA
320 to 290 million years ago

ice sheets

Karoo sea

icebergs

mountain glaciers

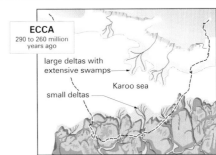

ECCA
290 to 260 million years ago

large deltas with extensive swamps

small deltas

Karoo sea

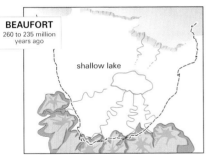

BEAUFORT
260 to 235 million years ago

shallow lake

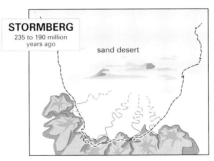

STORMBERG
235 to 190 million years ago

sand desert

Rocks that underlie the Great Karoo formed under a variety of conditions which ranged over time from glacial (Dwyka Group) to deltaic (Ecca Group) to river flood plain (Beaufort Group) to desert conditions (Stormberg Group).

WHY ARE THERE GLACIAL DEPOSITS IN SOUTH AFRICA?

No massive ice sheets covered southern Africa like those that blanketed much of the northern hemisphere during the last Ice Age (see page 114), so why should glacial deposits be found in South Africa? The answer to this question lies much further back in geological history.

The continents as we know them today are moving across the Earth's surface at an average rate of a few centimetres per year (see page 30). This may not sound like much, but in the context of geological time, which extends back thousands of millions of years, it is extremely rapid. As continents drifted around the globe, at times they have been swept together to form supercontinents. In their wanderings, they have sometimes passed over the poles. We know that the supercontinent Gondwana – comprising Africa, South America, Australia, Antarctica, India and Madagascar – once slid over the southern polar region. About 450 million years ago, what is today Morocco lay over the South Pole, but by 300 million years ago, what is now southern

Africa was in the same position. Gondwana continued moving northwards, so that southern Africa eventually emerged from the ice about 280 million years ago.

In very cold climates, snow accumulates and becomes compacted to form ice. Once the ice reaches a certain thickness, it is affected by gravity and begins to flow, becoming a valley glacier in mountainous terrain or a continental glacier in more open country, such as Greenland or Antarctica. These glacial ice sheets have immense erosive power, as have the rock fragments they carry within them. Rock fragments are ripped off the bedrock by the moving ice and are dragged along with it, where they help to shape and smooth the bedrock surface, grooving and scratching it in the process, as well as the rock fragments themselves. This grinding action forms fine, ground-up rock, known as rock flour. At the terminus of a glacier, the ice melts and its load of rock fragments and flour is dumped. Melt water from the glacier may wash the sediment flour away, and in the process sort it by size into gravel, sand and mud. Often, however, the dumped material remains intact, in which case it forms the characteristic unsorted mixture of large and small rock fragments in a very fine, almost mud-like matrix known as 'till' when it is newly formed, or 'tillite' when it is compacted into rock. Sometimes glaciers terminate into oceans as floating ice sheets, where blocks of ice regularly break off (calve) and float away as icebergs, particularly in summer. As the icebergs melt, their load of rock fragments and flour is dropped to the ocean floor where it forms typical unsorted tillite, or occasionally layered sedimentary deposits with isolated boulders.

As Gondwana passed under the icecap at the South Pole, the supercontinent experienced extensive glaciation. What is now southern Africa was subsiding at the time and a major period of sedimentation had begun. Had this not been the case, all evidence of glaciation may well have been lost. Instead, deposits that formed during glaciation were preserved, as were the surfaces over which the ice moved.

THE WORLD 300 MILLION YEARS AGO

Equator

drift direction

South Pole

From 450 to 280 million years ago, the African part of Gondwana moved across the South Pole and experienced glaciation. Resulting Dwyka Group glacial deposits are widely distributed across the country.

Glaciers carve rocks over which they flow into finely grooved, smooth surfaces, as can be seen in the glacial pavements near Barkley West in the Northern Cape (right) and Denny Dalton in KwaZulu-Natal (below). Boulders carried in the ice (centre right) are similarly smoothed and grooved.

Tillite, the rock equivalent of glacial till, is characterized by a jumbled assortment and size of rocks encased in a fine mud-like matrix, as seen at Denny Dalton (left) and Laingsburg in the Karoo (above).

These glacial deposits, collectively known as the Dwyka Group, are best developed in the southern Cape where they attain a thickness of almost 1 000 m. Here the glaciers were floating (see page 108), and thick layers of unsorted tillite are common. Dwyka deposits become thinner further north and are only sporadically developed. Glaciated rock surfaces (glacial pavements) are exposed where the lowermost tillite deposit has been removed by erosion, and are particularly well preserved where the glaciated rock is hard. Glacial pavements are well exposed along the Vaal River in the Barkly West area, for example at Nooitgedacht, and in parts of KwaZulu-Natal, for example at Denny Dalton and in Durban (University of KwaZulu-Natal, Westville Campus).

HAVE THERE EVER BEEN VOLCANOES IN SOUTHERN AFRICA?

Rather than being dotted randomly around the globe, volcanoes are mostly located in linear belts that lie along the boundaries of the Earth's tectonic plates (see page 40). They also occur at hot spots, which are situated directly above plumes of hot material rising from deep within the Earth. Southern Africa's position on the African tectonic plate is far from active plate boundaries, which means that there are no volcanoes in continental southern Africa. However, there are several hot spots in the offshore regions and these have produced the nearby volcanic islands of St Helena, Tristan da Cunha, Gough, Bouvet, Prince Edward and Marion.

Although there are no currently active volcanoes in southern Africa, the presence of ancient volcanic rock indicates that at times there has been volcanic activity in the region. The geological history of southern Africa is extremely long, having begun 3 644 million years ago with the formation of the oldest rocks. Since that time, rock sequences have been deposited more or less continuously, and many of these rocks are very well preserved. Some of the rocks are the result of lava eruptions over extensive areas, the first of which occurred 3 400 million years ago when undersea volcanoes spouted magma that solidified into the rocks of the Barberton region.

Lava to a depth of more than 1 km covered extensive areas of southern Africa during the formation of the Dominion Group 3 017 million years ago, the Ventersdorp Supergroup 2 714 million years ago, the Bushveld Complex 2 060 million years ago and the Karoo Supergroup 180 million years ago. There have also been many less voluminous volcanic events, such as the eruption of kimberlite intrusions over much of southern Africa between 110 and 90 million years ago (see page 82). This volcanic episode was responsible for the formation of most of the region's diamond deposits.

VOLCANIC ROCKS OF SOUTH AFRICA

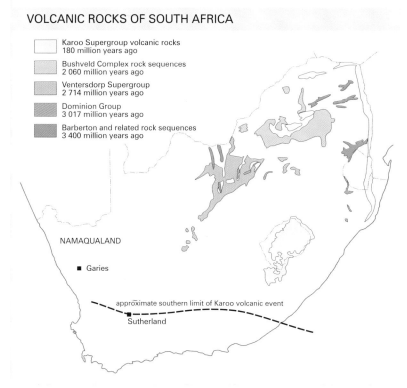

Karoo Supergroup volcanic rocks
180 million years ago

Bushveld Complex rock sequences
2 060 million years ago

Ventersdorp Supergroup
2 714 million years ago

Dominion Group
3 017 million years ago

Barberton and related rock sequences
3 400 million years ago

NAMAQUALAND

■ Garies

approximate southern limit of Karoo volcanic event

Sutherland

South Africa lies far from tectonic plate boundaries and mantle hot spots, so it has no active volcanoes – the last eruption occurred at Garies some 38 million years ago. But considerable volcanic activity occurred in the distant past, covering vast areas beneath hundreds of metres of lava, as shown on this map.

The most recent major volcanic event in southern Africa was the eruption of the Karoo lavas, which have largely been eroded away, but are still preserved and spectacularly exposed as the Maluti Mountains around Lesotho.

It was followed by further eruptions between 69 and 64 million years ago in the Northern Cape, mainly in the area north of Sutherland. The lava type that erupted is related to kimberlite, but does not contain diamonds. The most recent volcanoes in southern Africa erupted 38.5 million years ago near Garies in Namaqualand and 35.7 to 37 million years ago near Chamois Bay in Namibia.

Fossil frog from Stompoor

Crater fill sediment from Namaqualand

Between 64 and 69 million years ago, volcanic pipes erupted in the area from Sutherland northwards into Namaqualand. The volcanoes have long since been eroded away, but many craters contained lakes that accumulated sedimentary deposits, which today yield important fossils.

HOW DID THE LAST ICE AGE AFFECT SOUTHERN AFRICA?

SOUTHERN AFRICA DURING THE LAST ICE AGE

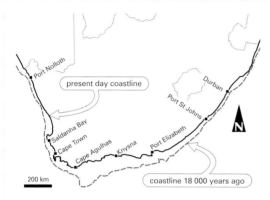

During the last Ice Age about 18 000 years ago, sea level was about 130 m lower than today, resulting in a very different coastline.

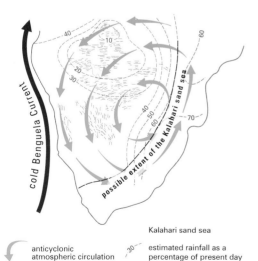

Kalahari sand sea

⌐ anticyclonic atmospheric circulation
30 estimated rainfall as a percentage of present day
linear dune
Okavango Delta

Southern Africa was much drier during the last Ice Age than it is now, and the Kalahari Desert was more extensive. Sand dunes formed a broad circular pattern due to strong anticyclonic winds.

Ice Ages are periods when the Earth's ice caps expand greatly, and they have occurred regularly over the past two million years. For at least the past 800 000 years, cold conditions interspersed with Ice Ages seem to have been the norm, but about every 100 000 years, warmer temperatures have prevailed. These so-called interglacial periods have generally lasted less than 10 000 years, and the Earth is currently experiencing one that has already endured for about that length of time (see page 56).

We know about Ice Ages and interglacial periods from the study of cores drilled in the Greenland and Antarctic ice caps (the isotopic composition of the hydrogen and oxygen forming the ice is directly related to the temperature at which the ice originally fell as snow). Cooling and warming periods in Greenland and Antarctica are mirrored by the surface temperature of the oceans around southern Africa, as revealed by the study of isotopes in microfossils in bottom sediment cores collected off the southern African coast.

The last Ice Age began about 120 000 years ago with a period of rapid global cooling (see page 58). Brief intervals of rapid temperature increases followed, interspersed with further periods of cooling that culminated in a global deep freeze about 18 000 years ago. At this time, much of North America, northern Europe and Siberia were buried beneath a sheet of ice several kilometres thick. This massive ice sheet locked up a huge amount of water, lowering sea level by about 130 m relative to today. The effects of the lower sea level around the southern African coast would have been quite dramatic: what is now Durban harbour would then have been 15 km from the sea, while the coastline would have lain about 45 km southeast of present-day Port Elizabeth (see page 62).

Although temperatures in southern Africa were several degrees colder than at present, there were no major ice sheets covering the land. The high mountains of Lesotho would have been subject to permafrost, and small glaciers may have developed in some of the south-facing mountain valleys. The seas were generally colder and the cold Benguela current extended much further north than today. The amount of moisture reaching the interior was therefore lower and the climate was much more arid, especially in the Kalahari region and in northern Botswana, eastern Angola and western Zambia, where rainfall may have been as low as 20% of the present value. The low rainfall reduced vegetation cover over much of the Kalahari, where the prevailing winds shaped the sand into long, linear dunes that can still be seen today. The Kalahari at that time was a true sand desert, devoid of vegetation, like the Namib of today. Taken as a whole, the pattern of dunes seems to define a large anticyclone, probably reflecting the stable, high-pressure atmospheric circulation over the region. The dunes provide some indication of just how arid the region was, because dunes of this type only form if the annual rainfall is less than about 150 mm per annum. It is likely that arid to semi-arid conditions extended well into what are now the Free State and Gauteng. The Kalahari sand sea in the interior extended to a latitude north of the Equator, forming what is today the most extensive sand body on Earth.

Warming began abruptly about 15 000 years ago, as the Ice Age ended, with a short-lived return to cold conditions between 12 000 and 11 000 years ago. Temperatures then rose again, and today's relatively warm conditions were attained about 10 000 years ago, along with an increase in rainfall over southern Africa and a

ANTARCTIC AND SOUTHERN AFRICAN OCEAN TEMPERATURES IN THE PAST

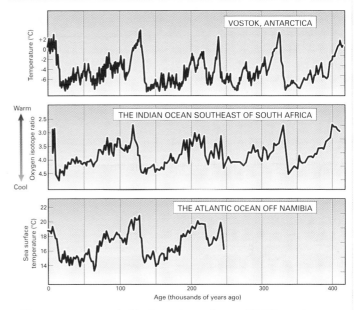

The temperature record of the Antarctic over the past 450 000 years has been deciphered from ice cores extracted from the area. This record of cooler and warmer episodes is also mirrored in sediment cores from the east and west coasts of southern Africa.

rise in sea level to its present position. Since then temperatures have been relatively stable, although both they and rainfall have shown some fluctuation. A maximum temperature, in the region of 1–2 °C warmer than today, was reached about 7 000 years ago. At this time, rainfall over the Kalahari was probably about 20% higher than it is at present. Gradually, however, conditions changed, and southern Africa became drier. A low point was reached in the Little Ice Age, which lasted from the early 1300s to the mid 1800s, and since then the temperature has apparently been rising.

Linear sand dunes that formed in the Kalahari sand sea during the last Ice Age are visible on satellite images, although they are now completely vegetated as can be seen along the Okavango River in northern Botswana and Namibia.

HOW HAS THE SOUTH AFRICAN LANDSCAPE CHANGED OVER TIME?

THE BREAKUP OF GONDWANA

140 million years ago

100 million years ago

60 million years ago

present

Gondwana began to break up about 180 million years ago, creating new oceans that profoundly affected global climate.

The oldest rocks in South Africa formed 3 644 million years ago, and continue to form in the region. These rocks tell us that South Africa has grown substantially since its genesis. It has been struck by large asteroids or comets, incorporated into supercontinents, buried under lava, submerged beneath the sea and beneath ice sheets several kilometres thick. It has also hosted majestic Himalayan-like peaks on several occasions. Above, the Earth's atmosphere has transformed from a toxic soup to an oxygenated one that allowed complex life to flourish. In fact, the South African landscape has witnessed almost the entire history of Earth, but its modern landscape began to form only about 180 million years ago, so our story will begin there.

At that time, southern Africa formed part of the Gondwanan supercontinent flanked by Antarctica, the Falklands Plateau and South America. The breakup of Gondwana was imminent (see page 30) and a vast 2 km-thick lava sheet covered our region, but it began to rupture where a volcanic plume was positioned, the point at which modern South Africa, Mozambique and Zimbabwe meet. By 140 million years ago Gondwana had split in two, creating the embryonic Indian Ocean, and 20 million years later, the Atlantic Ocean. As South America receded, the Falklands Plateau detached from the southern Cape and by 90 million years ago had fully separated from Africa.

Global climate at the time was warm and humid. Warm, shallow oceans surrounded southern Africa, creating an almost tropical climate inland, then about 2 000 m above sea level. Here, the ancestral Vaal-Orange River system had formed, while many short, coastal rivers were shaping the coastal plain. By 65 million years ago, a pronounced escarpment separated the interior plateau from the lower, eroded coastal plain, and the southern Cape Fold Mountains had been exhumed from beneath their cover of sedimentary rock. Warm, humid conditions supported conifer forests, and deep, tropical soils formed across the continent.

This balmy period abruptly ended 65 million years ago when an asteroid struck southern Mexico, a catastrophe that was soon followed by the eruption of huge volumes of lava in India, now known as the Deccan Traps. These combined effects largely destroyed the global ecosystem of the time. From the ashes a new world arose, where mammals and angiosperms replaced the previously dominant dinosaurs and gymnosperms. Southern Africa preserves no record of these events, however, because the continent was elevated and undergoing erosion, which erased all traces of the turmoil.

Interior uplift between 20 and 5 million years ago increased the elevation of southern Africa and greatly accentuated the escarpment, resulting in spectacular scenery such as in the Blyde River Canyon, Limpopo province.

Walter Knirr / IOA

COOLING OF THE ATMOSPHERE

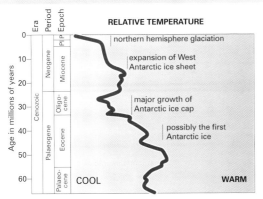

Isolation of the Southern Ocean and Antarctica caused global cooling, culminating in the Pleistocene Epoch of Ice Ages.

Global climate remained warm and temperature peaked about 55 million years ago, after which the Earth began to cool. Australia had separated from Antarctica and was moving steadily northwards, as was Africa. This opened the Southern Ocean and reduced the inflow of warm Pacific water into the Indian Ocean. South America and Antarctica separated about 35 million years ago, which opened the Drake Passage and allowed the Antarctic Circumpolar Current to form. Separated from warm equatorial waters, the Southern Ocean cooled and

In response to global cooling, the African savannas evolved, creating the environment for new animal species, including our Australopithecene ancestors.

Antarctica began to freeze, causing global cooling.

About 30 million years ago, the African continent ceased its northward drift and began to bulge upwards, especially in southern Africa, which rose in two pulses at about 20 and 5 million years ago respectively (see page 138). The uplift generated pulses of erosion in the interior that removed most of the thick, tropical soils, creating the topography we see today.

Cooling of the isolated Southern Ocean reduced the temperature of Benguela Current source waters, so it too became cooler, and as a result, westerly winds blowing inland off the South Atlantic became dry. The Namib Desert began to form, reaching its present arid state about 14 million years ago when upwelling of cold water began along the west coast. Uplift of the eastern escarpment exacerbated drying in the west, because it intercepted moisture from the warm Indian Ocean, thus establishing the east-to-west average rainfall gradient of 1 100 to 50 mm per year.

These climate changes fragmented the once extensive forests, which were replaced by grasslands and savannas. This in turn led to the evolution of a great variety and large numbers of grazing animals and their predators, because the carrying capacity of grassland vastly exceeds that of forest. Amongst the emergent animals was a group of tail-less apes, the ancestors of *Homo sapiens*, arriving with the birth of the African savanna ecosystem.

Meanwhile, cooling continued but accelerated from 2.5 million years ago, which marked the start of the Pleistocene Epoch of Ice Ages lasting for thousands of years at a time. During these periods, the sea level fell and the world became drier, particularly in southern Africa (see page 114). Perhaps it was during a glacial period that ancestral *Homo sapiens* evolved into modern man, who began to migrate from Africa into the wider world as a warmer, interglacial period dawned. The last Ice Age ended 10 000 years ago, and global climate has warmed dramatically since then, allowing humans to establish settlements, cultivate the land and lay the foundations for modern civilizations.

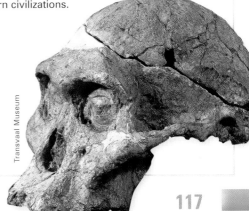

Transvaal Museum

117

WHAT GIVES VALLEYS THEIR DIFFERENT SHAPES?

Martin Harvey / IOA

In arid climates, erosion along lateral tributaries often cannot keep pace with a main river, resulting in steep lateral slopes such as in the Fish River Canyon of southern Namibia.

Valleys are primarily formed when glaciers, rivers, streams and rainwater cause erosion of the surface. The down-stream or longitudinal slope of a river from stream source to river mouth evolves constantly as water erodes its bed, tending to smooth and straighten its profile. Rivers usually feed into the sea, at which point erosion stops. This conduit is known as a graded profile, and over time, the source of the river will cut further inland, and the graded profile will gradually flatten out. All rivers have lateral tributaries, and these normally behave in unison with the main river, similarly flattening their longitudinal profiles over time. As they do so, the terrain between tributaries is lowered by hill slope processes, which involve slow, down-slope creep of soils, sheet wash during heavy storms, as well as landslides and avalanches in the case of steeper slopes. All these processes transport material towards tributary streams and hence to the main channel, from where it is transported to the sea. As a result, valleys gradually widen and generally evolve towards having gently sloping sides.

However, the local geology also influences the slopes of valley sides. Thus, wide, gently sloping valleys tend to occur in geologically stable environments with moist climates that favour perennial river flow, as well as softer, more easily weathered rocks amenable to efficient chemical breakdown and soil development. If chemically and mechanically resistant rock types are present, however, they tend to form steeper slopes, which recede by being undermined and then collapsing. In this way, deep gorges can form even under relatively moist climatic conditions, such as the Blyde River Canyon in Limpopo province. Furthermore, valley morphology can also change along a river's course as the local geology changes, and broad, open valleys can be interspersed with narrow gorges.

Rivers that flow through arid terrain provide a stark contrast. Such river systems strive toward a graded profile, but in the absence of moisture, lateral tributaries often cannot keep pace with erosion by the main river, so their longitudinal profiles become steep. Soils are generally thin or non-existent on the arid terrain between tributaries, and sheet wash rarely occurs because of low rainfall. Therefore, the major process causing valley-side retreat is undermining by the main river, leading to excessive steepening of hill slopes, which therefore collapse. Substantial debris flows induced by exceptionally heavy storms add to the erosion. Consequently, hill slopes tend to be steep, even where less resistant rock types form the valley walls, so these processes produce rugged, precipitous valleys, such as the Fish River Canyon of southern Namibia.

CHANGING RIVER GRADIENTS

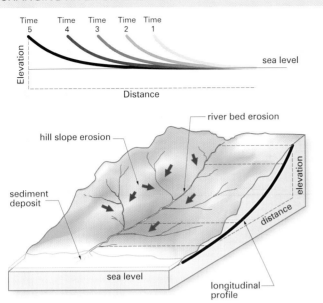

The gradient along a river from source to mouth evolves over time from short and steep to long and flat, as usually do its tributaries.

Unusual conditions can, however, cause variations on the two basic themes described above. A perennial river flowing through arid terrain that has experienced recent tectonic uplift can produce deep canyons with very steep valley slopes. The canyons of Arizona and Utah in the United States provide good examples of this. The Colorado River derives its water from snow melt in the Rocky Mountains and flows across the arid Colorado Plateau. Uplift of the Colorado Plateau commenced about 5 million years ago and the river began to slice downwards to restore its graded profile. Low rainfall on the plateau resulted in few lateral tributaries and poorly developed soils. Consequently the Colorado River has carved deep canyons on the plateau with extremely steep and rugged walls, the most famous being the Grand Canyon. Abundant perennial water coupled with uplift of the land has also resulted in spectacular gorges in the Himalayan range, such as on the upper Indus River.

Recent river incision in a relatively moist environment can also result in steep valley walls. The Orange River valley in Lesotho provides an example of this phenomenon. In this instance, it appears that down-cutting of the valley floor has been rapid. Lateral tributaries and valley slopes have lagged behind, accentuated by the locally hard rock, which has resulted in deep, steep-sided valleys. Steep valley walls such as these lend themselves to dam construction, which is a great boon to the thirsty Gauteng province.

The Grand Canyon in the USA formed as a result of uplift of the Colorado Plateau, through which the Colorado River cut. However, due to the arid climate, the tributaries could not keep pace with down-cutting, resulting in the spectacular canyon.

Relatively recent down-cutting along the upper Orange (Senqu) River in Lesotho has resulted in deep valleys suitable for dam construction, such as Khatse Dam.

HOW ARE SALT PANS FORMED?

Pans are shallow, circular or oval depressions that may contain water during rainy seasons, and range in diameter from tens of metres to many kilometres. They are widespread across southern Africa, but most occur in a belt extending from Bushmanland past Kimberley to Lake Chrissie in Mpumalanga, where the highest density of pans occurs. Pans also occur extensively in the Kalahari and throughout Botswana, where southern Africa's largest pan complex occurs – the Makgadikgadi Pans. Some pans only dry up during severe droughts, as is the case for Lake Chrissie. Elsewhere in the drier, western parts

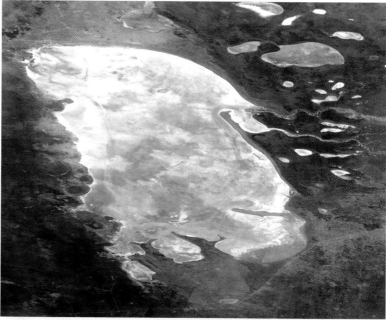

NASA

Salt pans are a common feature in southern Africa and can cover hundreds of square kilometres, such as Etosha in Namibia, seen here from space.

of South Africa, pans are usually dry and salt-encrusted, so when water is present, they become extremely saline. Remarkably, most pans are closed basins that have no outlet.

How pans form has intrigued geomorphologists for centuries. Most of South Africa is experiencing active erosion by flowing water, which erodes soil and rock and finally transports material to the oceans. However, flowing water is not responsible for pan formation, because pans have no outlet. Curiously, pans also occur in the Kalahari region where sediment accumulation is taking place, and has been for millions of years. Thus, pans form both where the land surface is being lowered by erosion or raised by sediment deposition. So why don't pans fill up with sediment?

Many different processes are responsible for pan formation. The Makgadikgadi Pans are remnants of a former lake the size of Lake Victoria, which formed 60 million years ago. However, due to changes in drainage lines that reduced inflow, coupled with increased general aridity in the region, the lake dried up. Wind-blown sand dunes then substantially reduced its size and fragmented it into a number of separate pans that now receive water only in particularly wet years. With no outlet,

all water is lost by evaporation, so salts accumulate and groundwater becomes extremely saline.

Natural loss of river systems may have produced some pans in South Africa, especially in the Kimberley area and around Lake Chrissie as well as in the Northern Cape province. This has been deduced from the way that some pans follow ancient river courses that long ago became fragmented into a series of dry pools, which subsequently became shallow pans due to redistribution of river sediment by wind and possibly also by animals.

Animal activity is also considered important in pan formation, as it remains in Etosha. In a semi-arid climate, vast herds of grazing animals were probably a formidable erosional force. Where depressions in the ground collect rainwater and attract animals, their grazing and trampling activities reduce vegetation cover and render drying depressions susceptible to wind erosion. Remaining muddy pools are used by animals to cake themselves with mud to reduce irritation from insect pests, but in so doing, material is removed. So, combined with wind erosion, pans form and become enlarged. Similar processes were probably particularly important in the formation

Lake Chrissie

The highest density of pans in southern Africa is in the Mpumalanga Lakes District near Chrissiesmeer. The largest is Lake Chrissie, at 6 km long.

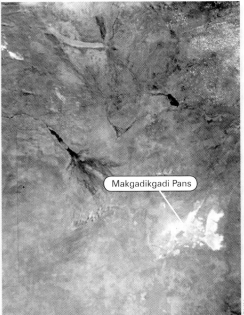

Makgadikgadi Pans

NASA

The largest pan in southern Africa is the Makgadikgadi Pan complex in Botswana, at about 200 km across.

When vast herds once roamed the region, animals were probably important erosive agents, gathering mud from wallows and transporting it away on their bodies.

of the Kalahari pans. Here, depressions may have been initiated by sand dune formation and once water had collected in the inter-dune depressions, combined environmental and animal activity would have facilitated pan formation.

In the Kalahari, barren pans often occur in close proximity to pans that are simply grassy depressions, leading to the notion that pans undergo a natural evolutionary cycle. Water-filled and vegetated pans that are frequented by many animals eventually become overgrazed, dusty, salt-encrusted depressions where the water becomes saline. Faced with brackish water, as well as overgrazed surroundings, the herds move on to another pan. Once free of animal influences, the pans begin to recover. Salts leach from the soil and burrowing insects and mammals restore the soil texture. Eventually grass encroaches across the pan, thus completing the cycle.

Water in pans comes principally from rainfall and runoff as well as groundwater, provided that the water table rises above the level of the pan floor. However, this may only occur during particularly wet periods (see page 128). Groundwater incursion does, however, often add to the salt load of the pan because it contains dissolved salts acquired from rocks through which the water percolates. The salinity of a pan reflects the net balance between evaporation and precipitation, and as evaporation exceeds rainfall over most of southern Africa, pans tend to become salty. This occurs more so in the west than the east because annual average rainfall in the Northern Cape is 50 to 100 mm, while evaporation exceeds 3 000 mm per year. Consequently, the area is arid and the pans are salty and cannot support plants, making the pan soils susceptible to wind erosion. Without vegetation to anchor it, sediment washed into the pan from any surrounding area is simply blown away when the pan dries, so pans don't fill with sediment.

Hein von Hörsten / IOA

HOW DO ROCK COLUMNS FORM?

Delicately balanced stacks of rocks often seen in hilly country, including some regions of the Karoo, conjure up visions of demons or giants idling away their time by playing with rocks. That not being the case, how then do rocks get to be apparently so precariously balanced? The answer is less fanciful – but no less interesting. Ironically, such piles of rock are formed by the removal of material rather than by construction from the bottom up.

Virtually all rock masses are criss-crossed by parallel cracks called joints, which are arranged vertically and horizontally in various orientations, and divide the rock mass into blocks of differing sizes and shapes. One form of jointing divides the rock into vertical, hexagonal columns called columnar jointing. The spacing between individual joints is very variable, ranging from just a few centimetres to many metres. Joints generally form in response to cooling and shrinking of the rock mass, as well as being due to gravitational unloading as erosion removes heavy overlying rocks. Joints are important because they provide access into the rock mass for water, air, various salts, roots, insects, and so forth.

Many minerals that form rocks are unstable in the presence of water and oxygen, and decompose in a series of chemical reactions collectively known as weathering, against which igneous rocks are the most susceptible. In this process, some chemical constituents are rendered soluble and are washed away, while the remaining material becomes a crumbly mass that is easily eroded. Weathering occurs preferentially, and therefore fastest, along joints because these provide passageways for the entry of water and air, particularly where three joints intersect. Weathering along joints therefore results in the unweathered core becoming rounded (a core stone), a process called spheroidal weathering.

On relatively flat ground, weathering along joints produces rounded core stones surrounded by a fairly thick skin of weathering products. Other core stones may become exposed on the land surfaces as the soft, surrounding material is removed by erosion. This results in a land surface littered with rounded boulders of varying sizes according to spacing intervals between the joints. However, on steeper slopes, erosion of the weathering skin is much faster and the joints

Columns of neatly stacked dolerite rock at Graaff-Reinet's Valley of Desolation, surrounded by the debris from collapsed columns.

Rock decomposition occurs preferentially along cracks, especially where three cracks intersect, resulting in spheroidal weathering of the core stone.

become etched out, leaving core stones piled upon each other, as if stacked by giant hands.

Igneous dolerite sills of the Karoo provide optimal conditions for the formation of piled core stones. Often found in the softer sedimentary strata of the Karoo Supergoup, they are characteristically well jointed, often by columnar jointing, while also being hard and very susceptible to chemical weathering. This contrast in hardness often produces flat-topped, dolerite-capped hills as the softer sedimentary strata hosting the dolerites are eroded away. The hard dolerites produce steep slopes or cliffs around the hilltops, which provide ideal conditions for the formation of stacked core stones, such as those at Graaff-Reinet's famous Valley of Desolation.

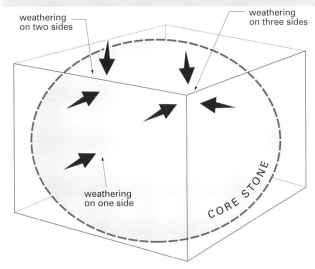

ROCK WEATHERING THAT FORMS A SPHERE

weathering on two sides

weathering on three sides

weathering on one side

CORE STONE

Preferential weathering along cracks leaves hard core stones surrounded by soft, decomposed material.

THE FORMATION OF ROCK COLUMNS

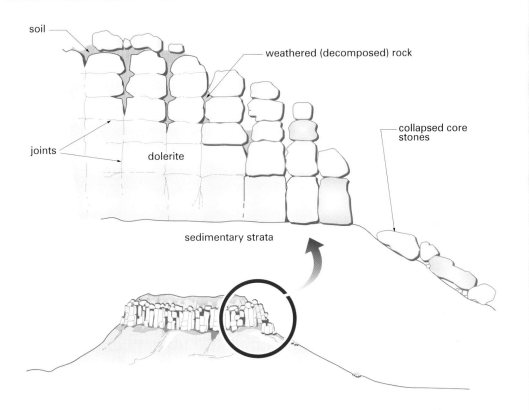

soil

weathered (decomposed) rock

collapsed core stones

joints

dolerite

sedimentary strata

On steep slopes, weathered filling cracks and is washed away by rain, leaving core stones in a stacked arrangement.

WHAT CAUSES SINKHOLES?

Sinkholes form when the land surface suddenly collapses into an underground cavity that has been created by subterranean erosion. They can range from being smaller than a square metre, to more than a hectare in area, and commonly occur in areas underlain by dolomite or limestone bedrock. These rock types are slightly soluble in groundwater, and slowly dissolve to form underground caverns; these are initially filled with water, but later drain and become air-filled (see page 134). Soil generally overlies the cavernous bedrock, and may either creep slowly into cavities in the underlying rock, forming gradually subsiding depressions (dolines), or it may be temporarily held by stable bridges over the voids. Eventually, however, such bridges give way, resulting in catastrophic collapse of the surface. In urban areas, leaking pipes often accelerate collapse of soil bridges by eroding them from below, so thinning them to the point of collapse. Another cause of sinkholes in urban areas is due to seepage and consequent erosion in underground storm-water drains, which enlarges the drains, eventually leading to surface collapse.

SINKHOLE FORMATION

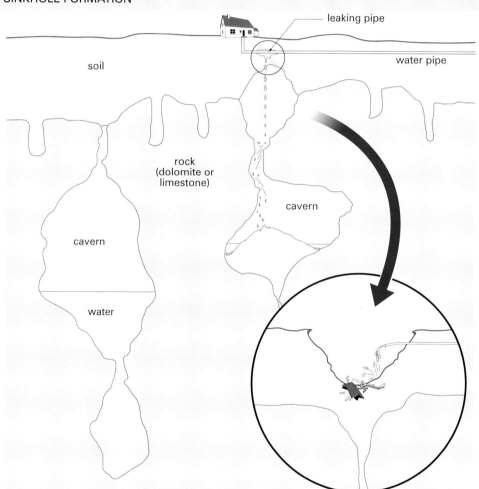

Most sinkholes occur in areas underlain by dolomite or limestone. These rock types are slightly soluble in groundwater and dissolve, forming underground cavities. Soil often forms bridges over these cavities, but they eventually collapse, resulting in sinkholes.

Small sinkholes are sometimes associated with – and help to accelerate – soil erosion. This is particularly evident in the eastern Free State, where huge dongas are a common feature of the landscape. Valley soils in this area have an unusual property: when immersed in water, they rapidly disaggregate and disperse, hence their name, 'dispersive soils'. During dry periods, deep vertical cracks form in the valley soils as a result of shrinkage, and these cracks often connect through to stream gullies. Rainwater flowing across the land surface enters such cracks and then flows along them into the gulley or donga. Water disintegrates the soil along these crack walls and widens them into pipe-like cavities – a phenomenon called piping. Over time, the pipes enlarge and eventually parts of their roofs collapse, forming sinkholes. These eventually interconnect to form dongas.

Right: Leaking pipes accelerate collapse of material into underground cavities, so buildings can fall victim to sinkholes, such as this tennis club at Venterspost, West Rand, in 1970.

Below and below right: Certain types of soil readily disintegrate in water and are prone to sinkhole and donga formation.

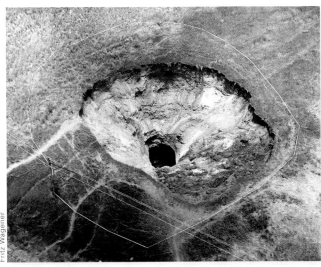

Fritz Wagener

Sinkholes are fairly common features in dolomitic areas in Gauteng and further west, and usually appear without warning.

Fritz Wagener

Terence McCarthy

Terence McCarthy

HOW ARE RIVERS FORMED?

When rain falls, some soaks deep into the ground to become groundwater (see page 128), while some wets the near-surface soil, and vegetation returns much of this to the atmosphere by evapotranspiration. The remaining water leaves the land surface by runoff. The proportion of runoff varies widely, both from place to place and seasonally. Places with hard, impervious soils produce more runoff than do pervious soils, while there is also more runoff from saturated soils, as occurs during Cape winters. Cities and towns also generate a huge amount of runoff because roofs and paved surfaces do not allow water to soak away into the ground. This is why suburban rivers in many parts of South Africa are prone to sudden rises in water level during storms, occasionally with tragic and destructive consequences.

Rivers function as conduits to drain this excess surface water by creating paths for themselves in the form of river valleys, which they create by erosion of the landscape. Sometimes, however, there is no excess surface water and therefore no rivers. This can be the case in areas underlain by limestone or dolomite rock, which are slightly soluble in water. In such areas an underground drainage system often develops, and all rainwater soaks into the ground (see page 128).

Rivers are constantly eroding their valleys, which extends them upstream, and, in the process, they lower the land surface (see page 118). They may also compete with each other, and one river may capture another by eroding back into a less dominant river flow (see page 140). Rivers therefore play an important role in shaping the Earth's surface. Occasionally, major changes can be caused by a single flood, but really important changes occur on extremely slow geological time scales. Therefore the river networks we observe are the product of thousands or even millions of years of erosion and it is often difficult to establish why a river flows where it does. This is especially the case in southern Africa, where the land surface is extremely old. Answers to why rivers flow where they do are usually complex and more often than not, are lost in the mists of time (see page 140).

Rivers carry excess surface water, but they are also connected to the groundwater. How does this occur and what regulates water exchanges between these two separate but coupled systems? Below the depth of the water table, all pore spaces in the soil or rock are filled with water (see page 128), while conversely, soils and rocks above the water table

Rivers draining urban areas are prone to sudden floods during heavy thunderstorms, a phenomenon dramatically illustrated by the stream at the Walter Sisulu Botanical Gardens on the Witwatersrand.

are not saturated. So, if the water surface of a river is at a level higher than the water table, water seeps through the river bed and feeds the groundwater. As long as there is surface water, this process will continue until the groundwater level is the same as that of the river, when no further seepage will occur. But if the groundwater reservoir is large and empty, water will continue to seep through the river bed,

LOSING STREAM

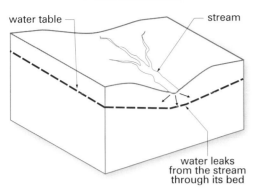

GAINING STREAM

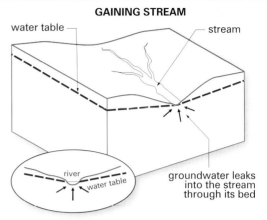

Losing streams supplied only by rainfall run-off tend to lose water by seepage into the ground and are ephemeral, whereas gaining rivers supplied by groundwater are perennial.

so gradually decreasing the downstream river volume unless it is topped up by tributaries or rainfall runoff. If this does not happen, the rivers or streams eventually become dry and these are known as 'losing streams'. The converse occurs when the water table is at a higher level than the water level in the river. If so, groundwater seeps through the river bed into the river, adding to its downstream volume. Such rivers are known as 'gaining streams'.

Surface runoff provides some or all of the water carried in rivers, although this may be augmented by groundwater as described above. Gaining streams that are linked to large groundwater reservoirs are less dependent on runoff and so flow is perennial, whereas losing streams are supplied by runoff and are generally seasonal or even ephemeral if infiltration is extreme. However, during prolonged droughts, the water table may fall to below the bed of a gaining stream, in which case it will dry up, as can even happen to normally perennial rivers.

A single river can, however, be both gaining and losing along its course. This usually happens where a river's source is in a high-rainfall region where it gains groundwater, but then flows into an arid region where it loses its water to the groundwater. Such rivers are common in Namibia because most rivers rise in the higher rainfall escarpment area, and then flow west into the Namib Desert, where they disappear in the dunes. The Okavango River is another example of this, as it rises in the highlands of Angola where groundwater inflow renders it perennial. But as it flows through Namibia and especially Botswana, it loses water, which eventually disappears into the Kalahari sands beneath the Okavango Delta. In contrast, the Thukela (Tugela) River rises high in the Drakensberg, and is fed both by groundwater inflow and by tributaries of similar nature along its entire length, so its volume increases steadily from source to mouth.

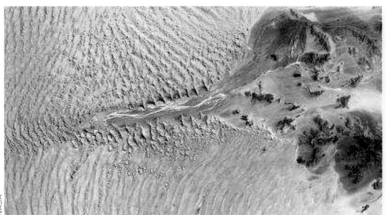

Rivers rising in the Namibian Highlands flow westwards, losing water as they go, eventually dying in the sands of the Namib Desert.

WHY IS THERE WATER UNDER GROUND?

Windmill-driven boreholes used to obtain groundwater are a familiar and iconic sight on many Karoo farms where piped municipal water is unavailable. Alternatively, farmers sometimes use motor-driven pumps to do the same job, while before the advent of borehole drilling machines, farmers laboriously dug wells to obtain water. The life-giving importance of wells cannot be underestimated, but quaint notions about groundwater abound. Especially common is the idea that rivers under ground can easily be tapped by boreholes, and, although such rivers do exist, they are uncommon and restricted to certain kinds of bedrock.

Groundwater occurs because of the nature of soils and rocks. Surface soils consist of decomposed rock that has been biochemically modified. Deeper down, biochemical processes are less active, so rock fragments are present. The soil and rock fragment layer is called the regolith, which varies in thickness from zero where underlying bedrock outcrops, to tens of metres thick. Bedrock is rarely completely solid and usually contains openings. Rocks such as sandstones may be very porous, whereas others such as granite allow water penetration only through open cracks (joints) and fissures, but most rocks have some degree of porosity.

Most rainfall returns to the atmosphere by evapotranspiration, but about 20% soaks into the ground and percolates down through the regolith as far as it can, filling all available voids. In this way, rock cavities below the regolith (and even deeper) fill with water, as long as there is sufficient water. The depth to which all voids fill with water is called the water table, and this depth varies widely. In arid areas it can be tens of metres deep, but on the banks of perennial rivers or along dam shorelines, the water table is at the surface. Elsewhere, springs or seepage lines form where the water table also reaches the surface. Where the landscape is flat, the water table mostly follows surface contours, but it is deeper under hills and shallower in valleys because groundwater flows slowly from the former to the latter.

The zone of rock and regolith that contains groundwater is called an aquifer. In South Africa, rock fractures form most aquifers, although in some coastal areas, porous sand dunes provide good aquifers. As one might expect, the storage capacity of a highly fractured rock aquifer is more than that of a less fractured one. Clearly, too, the storage volume will be larger where adjacent rock fractures are connected.

The water table depth is usually seasonably variable, rising in the rainy season, but falling in the dry season as groundwater discharges into streams (see page 126). However, in desert regions such as the Sahara Desert, the groundwater recharge rate is very low indeed and water contained in its aquifers accumulated there during wetter conditions that prevailed prior to 5 000 years ago when the Sahara was a savanna dotted with numerous lakes. Such 'fossil' groundwater will eventually be exhausted if

Rainfall seeps through the porous regolith and accumulates as groundwater in pores and cracks in the rocks and regolith, filling all voids below the water table.

HOW WATER ACCUMULATES UNDER GROUND

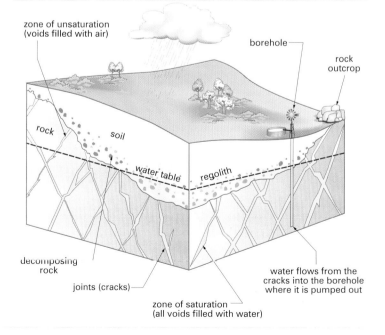

zone of unsaturation (voids filled with air)

borehole

rock outcrop

rock

soil

water table

regolith

decomposing rock

joints (cracks)

zone of saturation (all voids filled with water)

water flows from the cracks into the borehole where it is pumped out

Hein von Hörsten / IOA

In the dry Karoo, outlying communities often rely on windmills to obtain groundwater for drinking and for livestock.

extracted or 'mined'. Libya's Great Man-made River is an example of this sort of dubious undertaking – a network of pipes that supplies water from the Sahara Desert in Libya, by tapping into the vast fossil aquifer.

Boreholes are normally drilled to a depth well below the water table, and refill naturally with water from the surrounding aquifer to that level as water is pumped out. The maximum yield (litres per minute) of a borehole is reached when the extraction rate equals the refill rate. This rate is high in extensive, very porous aquifers, but low in aquifers that are small or of low porosity, and especially where the interconnectivity between pore spaces is low. Excessive abstraction lowers the water table, and if this falls below the level of the pump inlet, water cannot be extracted and the borehole becomes dry. This usually happens during droughts when the groundwater recharge rate is low, but a return of wet conditions will raise the water table and the borehole will again yield water. But there are aquifers that can yield even larger volumes without using pumps.

Dolomite and limestone bedrock are slightly soluble in groundwater and slowly dissolve, especially where water penetrates along fractures

(see page 134), eventually forming huge caves that fill with water. Large interconnected caves can provide a massive water resource, forming what is essentially an underground lake and river system that may emerge as springs such as the Fountains in Pretoria, the Eye of Kuruman, Maloney's Eye near Magaliesberg or Oog van Skoonspruit at Ventersdorp. Many such springs are sought after because of their water quality.

Groundwater quality is, however, very variable and generally related to climate. In arid areas the groundwater is often very saline because of evapotransporative water loss from the groundwater, which concentrates dissolved salts, sometimes making the water too salty for human consumption. In wetter areas, however, water quality is generally exceptionally good. In certain areas, fresh groundwater floats on denser saline water. This is the case throughout the Okavango Delta in Botswana, where shallow boreholes provide good quality water, but not if they are drilled too deeply: although the groundwater is saline from high evapotranspiration rates, the Okavango River constantly provides a layer of fresh water above the saline water.

THE ORIGIN OF DOLOMITE SPRINGS

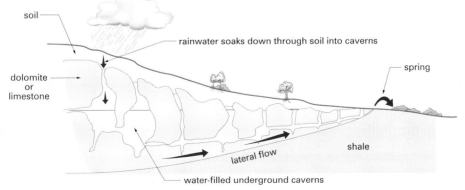

Dolomite and limestone slowly dissolve in water, creating interconnected underground cave systems, which often collect vast reservoirs of groundwater that can discharge as strong springs.

WHY IS SOME RIVER WATER TEA COLOURED?

There are two different phenomena that give natural colour to river water, these being the presence of muddy sediment in suspension, and coloured substances dissolved in water. They are easily distinguished because water containing sediment in suspension is turbid or cloudy, whereas water containing dissolved coloured substances is clear, like tea without milk. Muddy sediment is derived from the erosion of clay-rich soils and is particularly evident in the Orange River. Coloured compounds in water are generally derived from organic matter, although some natural minerals can enhance the colours.

Water in the rivers draining the mountainous regions of the southern Cape is usually tea-coloured, but clear. The colour is due to the presence of various brown- to yellow-coloured organic compounds known as tannins, humic acids, fulvic acids and phenols derived from fynbos. Some tannins are acidic and the pH of river water containing them is typically in the range 5 to 6. Several of these compounds may bind with normally insoluble metals, particularly iron, which can enhance the brown colour.

Soils of the southern Cape region are of poor quality, being very sandy and very low in nutrients, because they form from Cape mountain sandstones. However, the endemic and hardy Cape fynbos vegetation is adapted to these poor soils and thrives in the Mediterranean-like climate. When fynbos plants die, the fibrous vegetation decays slowly in the acidic soils, so much of the soil is composed

Terence McCarthy

A typical tea-coloured stream in the southwestern Cape.

The relatively clear water of the Vaal River mixes slowly with muddy Orange River water at their confluence.

Terence McCarthy

During summer floods, peat-stained brown water is flushed from the permanent swamps of the Okavango Delta, contrasting dramatically with the normally crystal-clear swamp water.

of partially decayed plant material, giving it a peaty character. This also imparts sponge-like properties to the soils, which accumulate water during the winter rainy season, releasing it slowly into streams together with the non-toxic and brown-coloured soluble decay products. The colour imparted varies seasonally, generally becoming darker during the dry season when dilution by rainwater runoff is minimal, while in winter, the rivers are fast-flowing, clear and cold.

Similar coloration of both surface and shallow groundwater occurs in and around the peat swamps of the Okavango Delta in northern Botswana. The peat can be up to several metres thick, and consists of a fibrous mat of plant material with very little mineral matter. During seasonal floods, water flows through the peat beds and out onto the surrounding flood plains, carrying with it dissolved organic compounds, which sometimes give the water a reddish-brown colour.

Water in streams draining the fynbos regions of the Western Cape is usually tea coloured, but clear.

HOW ARE SAND RIPPLES PRESERVED IN ANCIENT ROCKS?

Fossilized ripple marks are found in sedimentary rocks of all ages, and in South Africa examples have been recorded in virtually all rock sequences, from the 3 200 million-year-old Moodies Group to the roughly 100 million-year-old Zululand Group. Ripples form in sediment as a result of the action of wind or flowing water, and they are most commonly formed in silt and sand of fine to medium grain size. Coarse sand and gravel seldom bear rippled surfaces. Ripples vary in their size and shape depending on the conditions under which they were formed. In general, ripple size increases with an increasing level of wind or water disturbance.

The preservation of ripples occurs when ripple-marked sand or silt layers become buried by a thin layer or film of muddy material, followed by successive layers of sand or silt. The introduction of a cementing medium by water, or deep burial and heating, transforms the sand or silt and mud into rock, while generally keeping intact the internal structures of the rock. During subsequent erosion, parting of the rock often occurs along the plane of the mudstone film, resulting in a rippled surface and its negative impression, which are often seen in overhanging outcrops of sedimentary rock. In effect, the mudstone film acts as a releasing agent, in much the same way as butter is used in baking trays to allow separation of the cookies from the tray.

Ripple-marked surfaces in sand or silt may also be buried beneath a mud layer of substantial thickness. The resulting mudstone is generally more easily decomposed by weathering than siltstone and sandstone, and during weathering and erosion of the sedimentary rock strata, the ripple-marked surface becomes exposed as the covering mudstone layer is removed.

Carl Anhaeusser

Fossil ripple marks are visible in 3 200 million-year-old sedimentary rocks from Barberton.

PRESERVATION OF RIPPLES IN ROCK

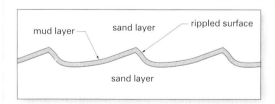

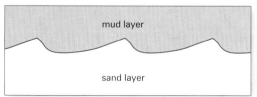

When a rippled surface on sand is buried by a layer of mud, followed by more sand and then further burial of the layers, hard rock is eventually formed. During subsequent weathering and erosion of the rock, the preserved ripples become exposed.

Sand ripples on Noordhoek beach, Cape Town.

Fossilized ripples in 2 400 million-year-old siltstone from Mpumalanga.

Large fossilized ripples in 2 950 million-year-old sandstone from KwaZulu-Natal.

HOW DO CAVES, STALACTITES AND STALAGMITES FORM?

The Cango and Sterkfontein caves are formed in dolomite [$CaMg(CO_3)_2$] or limestone (calcite, $CaCO_3$) rocks because such carbonate-based rocks are soluble in acids. So where, then, does the acid come from to do this? Firstly, carbon dioxide (CO_2) in the atmosphere dissolves in rainwater as it falls to Earth. As the rainfall percolates through surface soils also containing CO_2, the water becomes further enriched with dissolved CO_2, which combines with the water to form weak carbonic acid (H_2CO_3). This is described by the following chemical equation:

$$1.\ H_2O + CO_2 = H_2CO_3$$

Carbonic acid then dissolves limestone and dolomite to form soluble calcium bicarbonate [$Ca(HCO_3)_2$] and soluble magnesium bicarbonate [$Mg(HCO_3)_2$], as described in the next two equations:

$$2.\ H_2CO_3 + CaCO_3 = Ca(HCO_3)_2$$
$$3.\ 2H_2CO_3 + CaMg(CO_3)_2 = Ca(HCO_3)_2 + Mg(HCO_3)_2$$

As carbonic acid is very weak, the dissolution process is slow; furthermore, the solubility of calcium bicarbonate is low, so the amount of rock that can be dissolved in rainwater is small.

Rocks below surface soils are seldom completely solid, and usually contain cracks and fractures that become filled with rainwater up to the level of the water table (see page 128). Below the water table, walls of the cracks in limestone or dolomite dissolve in the weak carbonic acid, causing the cracks gradually to widen. The water soon becomes saturated in calcium bicarbonate and dissolution would stop; however, as groundwater slowly percolates from elevated to low-lying regions, it is replaced by unsaturated rainwater that can dissolve more rock. In low-lying areas, groundwater may discharge as a spring, or through a river bed (see page 126). Springs can be quite spectacular, discharging large quantities of extremely high-quality water, such as the Eye of Kuruman or the Fountains at Pretoria (see page 128). Such springs must be recharged by rainfall to maintain their high flow rates, so in these systems, the capacity to carve out large, water-filled caverns in dolomite or limestone rocks by carbonic acid dissolution is therefore substantial. Very deep-seated cracks in these rocks also contain water, but as this is largely static, it becomes saturated in calcium bicarbonate, so dissolution ceases. Thus cavern formation is generally restricted to just below the water table where most groundwater flow occurs.

As these processes take place, the land surface is also steadily lowered by water erosion, particularly in river valleys. Where this happens, spring discharge points are lowered, so the water table falls. As a result, caverns once filled with water may partially or completely drain, forming underground lakes such as at the Sterkfontein Caves, or simply open caves. As the water table falls further, new deeper caverns form to create, eventually, a network of descending open caves and water-filled caverns.

Once a cavern is partially or fully drained, new chemical processes start to operate. Rainwater percolating through the ground as weak carbonic acid dissolves limestone and dolomite in transit (equations 2 and 3), but also becomes saturated with CO_2 acquired from the soil. This means the water now contains more CO_2 than it would have if simply dissolving CO_2 from

Bernie Olbrich / Afripics.com

Caves underlain by dolomite and limestone form networks of water-filled cavities, which may discharge as springs such as the Eye of Kuruman.

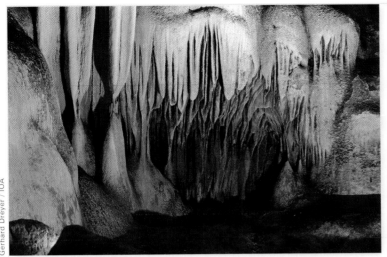

Stalactites and stalagmites form and grow where calcium carbonate deposits precipitate as water drips from the roof and onto the floor, respectively. Water flowing down the cave wall produces curtains of calcite flowstone, as in the Cango Caves.

the air alone. Some of this CO_2 and mineral-rich water finds its way into underground caverns where it seeps through the roof of the cavern and either flows down the walls or drips from the roof. When the water comes into contact with normal air, it loses (degases) CO_2 into the air to restore the CO_2 equilibrium between water and air. Carbon dioxide degassing causes precipitation of dissolved calcium carbonate as a residue that remains on the cave wall or roof. These processes are described by the following chemical equation:

$$4.\ Ca(HCO_3)_2\ \text{(dissolved)} = CaCO_3\ \text{(solid)} + H_2O\ \text{(liquid)} + CO_2\ \text{(gas)}$$

Where water flows down the cavern wall, calcium carbonate precipitates as a curtain or flowstone on the wall that may take on convoluted shapes reflecting the water flow paths. Where drops fall from the roof, calcium carbonate residues form stalactites, while stalagmites similarly form and rise from the floor where drops land. In time, stalactites and stalagmites may meet and form a column from floor to roof. These deposits are collectively known as speleothems. Magnesium bicarbonate is much more soluble than calcium bicarbonate, so magnesium bicarbonate does not precipitate in dolomite caverns.

In this way, caverns fill with spectacular formations of pure white calcium carbonate, often adorned with delicate crystal clusters, or sometimes stained by red iron oxide. The Cango Caves have spectacular cave formations, but many caves in the Sterkfontein area, including Sterkfontein itself, were mined for their very pure calcium carbonate, and most cave formations were unfortunately removed.

Ultimately, the cavern roof collapses, forming rubble or debris cones on the cave floor. These steadily grow, even as more soil material enters from above, gradually filling the cave, and sometimes forming a surface sinkhole (see page 124). Caves may eventually fill completely in this way. Amongst the material that fell into the caverns of the Sterkfontein area were animals, including human ancestors, and excavations have yielded more hominid fossils there than anywhere else in Africa.

Caves form by dissolution of limestone or dolomite below the water table, and may later partially drain, forming underground lakes, such as those at Sterkfontein.

WHAT IS THE TOPOGRAPHY OF THE SEA BED?

People have been interested in the topography of the sea bed ever since the building of large ships began. It was necessary to know the depth of the sea to avoid grounding of these vessels, so bathymetric charts of the world's oceans were steadily compiled by seafaring nations over many centuries. The standard method used was to lower a weighted line to the sea floor, hence the phrase 'swinging the lead'. This method provided fairly good charts of the relatively shallow waters around continents that extend to about 100–200 m in depth, but the floor of the deep oceans (up to 4 km or more beneath the ocean surface) remained a mystery. However, the invention of echo sounding (sonar) and its application to ocean bathymetry increased rapidly during and after World War II in the 1940s and began to provide fascinating insight into ocean floor topography. Topographic maps of the ocean floors first began to appear in the late 1950s and early 1960s, but these were greatly improved as ships added more depth-sounding data over the following 70 years. Satellite imagery has, however, transformed our view of the ocean floors. Satellite altimeters very precisely map the average height of the sea surface to within a few centimetres, which mirrors the underlying topography, so that very accurate maps of the ocean floor can now be drawn up.

Such maps reveal that the continents are surrounded by a continental shelf of comparatively shallow water, which extends from as little as a few hundred metres offshore where the shelf is narrow, to perhaps 100 km or more where the shelf is wide, for example the Falklands Plateau on which the Falkland Islands are located. At its edge, often called the shelf break, the continental shelf ends abruptly and depth plunges rapidly to the abyssal plain at about 4 000 m, on average. Continental shelves have many interesting topographic features. For example, the South African continental shelf is transected by several deep canyons, such as the Cape Canyon; and there are also large, dune-like features running parallel to the coast lines (see pages 62 and 98). There appear to be detached portions of continental shelf in the ocean basins, such as the Agulhas and Mozambique plateaus lying to the south and southeast of South Africa. The Agulhas Plateau is believed to be a fragment of continental crust that became detached from Africa during the breakup of Gondwana (see page 30), while the Mozambique Plateau might have similar origins.

Despite their name, abyssal plains are far from flat. Their most striking feature is the mid-ocean ridge system, which is a continuous undersea mountain range extending across all the oceans. It is about 70 000 km long, about 1 500 km wide, and typically rises to about 3 000 m above the flanking abyssal plains. It appears above sea level in only one place, where it forms the island of Iceland. Mid-ocean ridges have a pronounced central rift valley and are broken up into segments by cracks that are more

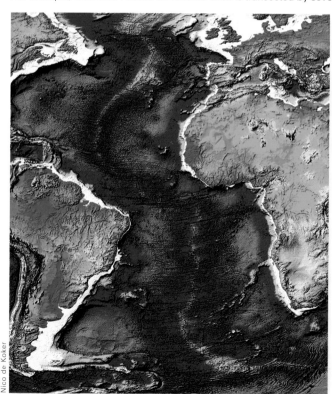

Nico de Koker

The Atlantic Ocean is neatly bisected by the Mid-Atlantic Ridge, a mountain range that rises several thousand metres above the abyssal plains.

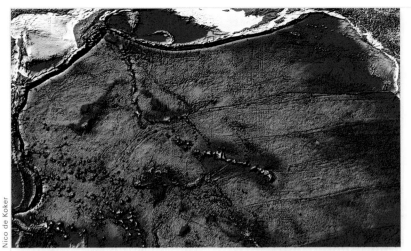

Nico de Koker

The floor of the northern Pacific Ocean is characterized by a deep trench flanked on its landward side by the volcanic Japanese and Aleutian Islands, and deep abyssal plains to the south peppered with undersea extinct volcanoes.

Prominent features of the ocean floor off the coast of southern Africa include the Walvis Ridge, the volcanic islands of Gough and Tristan da Cunha, the wide Agulhas Bank and the shallow Mozambique Plateau.

or less perpendicular to the central valley. Some of these can be traced for thousands of kilometres across the sea floor. Also present are deep trenches, especially around the Pacific Ocean, and it is in these trenches that the greatest ocean depths are attained, such as the 11 km-deep Mariana Trench east of the Philippines. Deep trenches sometimes flank continents, such as those that follow the west coast of South America. Elsewhere, off the southeast coast of Japan, deep trenches are found alongside chains of volcanic islands. Abyssal plains are also studded with sea mounts, often arranged in long chains with active volcanic islands at one end, such as the Emperor and Hawaiian chains, or even continuous ridges such as the Walvis Ridge off the coast of Namibia. The undersea mountain of Hawaii is in fact the tallest mountain in the world.

The topography of the ocean floor has proved to be the Rosetta Stone of geology and has had a profound influence on the way we view Earth. Maps revealing the existence of mid-ocean ridges led to the idea that continents drift apart by sea floor spreading from the ridges. The theory was tested in the early 1960s, using the observation that the magnetic poles had periodically reversed in the past (see page 22), and it was found to be correct. Later, the concept of sea floor spreading was succeeded by the more comprehensive theory of plate tectonics, which has transformed our understanding of the Earth and the processes that operate within it (see page 30).

Nico de Koker

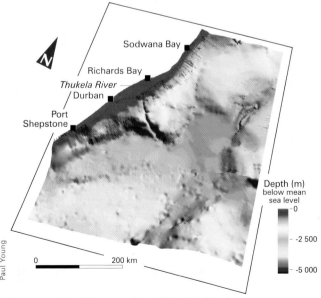

Paul Young

The topography of the ocean floor off KwaZulu-Natal, showing the Thukela (Tugela) canyon.

HOW DID SOUTH AFRICA'S STEEP EASTERN ESCARPMENT FORM?

In broad terms, southern Africa consists of an interior plateau generally lying more than 1 000 m above sea level, separated from the lower-lying surroundings by a distinct escarpment. The interior plateau slopes gently from west to east. The escarpment rises abruptly from about 700 m to 1 900 m in the Blyde River Canyon area, and from about 300 m to about 1 000 m in the area west of Springbok. This plateau has its origins in the breakup of Gondwana between 120 and 140 million years ago (see page 116). At that time the elevation of the region may have been as high as 2 000 m above sea level. The opening of the Indian Ocean began with the formation of a rift valley along what is now the Lebombo Mountains in Mozambique about 120 million years ago and created a narrow coastal plain, flanked by the high shoulder of the rift bordering the elevated interior. Rivers formed and began to erode the shoulder back, forming an escarpment that separated a widening coastal plain from the interior. The climate was warm and humid, and the escarpment was eroded back almost to its present position by about 60 million years ago. The interior plateau also experienced lowering due to erosion. Thereafter, climate change dramatically slowed the rate of retreat of the escarpment (see page 116).

The western escarpment near Clanwilliam (top) rises about 700 m, whereas the eastern escarpment near Hoedspruit (left) rises more than 1 000 m in a near-vertical wall.

Below: Southern Africa consists of an interior plateau lying above 1 000 m elevation and tilted downwards towards the west, fringed by lower-lying terrain.

PROFILE ON LATITUDE 26°S

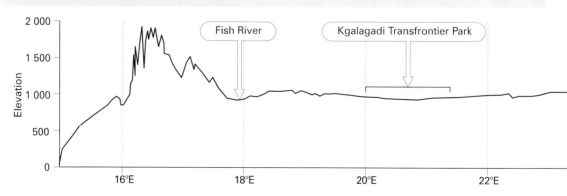

The eastern escarpment in the KwaZulu-Natal area is very steep, in this case accentuated by a thick capping of basaltic lavas which form the Maluti Mountains.

Most of the major rivers on the interior plateau flowed to the west (see page 140), while the eastern escarpment had only short rivers rising close to its edge, which largely ensured its uniform retreat. The Limpopo River was an important exception, and erosion by this river and its tributaries pushed the escarpment far into the interior along the Limpopo River valley.

The subcontinent experienced two episodes of uplift at about 20 and 5 million years ago respectively, which increased the height of the eastern escarpment by about 1 000 m and the western escarpment by about 300 m. Uplift also had the effect of tilting the coastal plain seaward, especially in the east. The cause of this uplift is uncertain but appears to be related to events deep in the mantle below southern Africa where a plume of hot material still seems to be developing.

The escarpment varies in character along its length. In the Limpopo River valley, it is gentle and hardly perceptible because of back-cutting by this river system. Elsewhere, its character is strongly influenced by the local geology. In Mpumalanga,

especially in the Blyde River Canyon area, it rises like a sheer wall. The steepness here is a consequence of thick layers of very tough quartzite lying on more easily weathered granite. Quartzite does not decompose easily and is strong, so the escarpment retreats by undermining and episodic collapse of the cliff faces. Similar features can be seen further south in the Waterval-Boven area. Still further to the south, the tough quartzites disappear, and the escarpment is formed of much softer sedimentary rocks of the Karoo Supergroup, and accordingly it has a gentler slope, such as in the Van Reenen's Pass area. The escarpment again steepens in the KwaZulu-Natal Drakensberg, where hard volcanic rocks overlie soft sedimentary rocks. Here, volcanic rocks form a near vertical wall locally reaching 1 600 m in height. The elevation of this section of the escarpment bordering Lesotho is much higher than elsewhere (about 3 000 m) because of the presence of a large remnant of an ancient, older land surface in this region formed by basalt lavas, which create the Maluti Mountains. (see page 116).

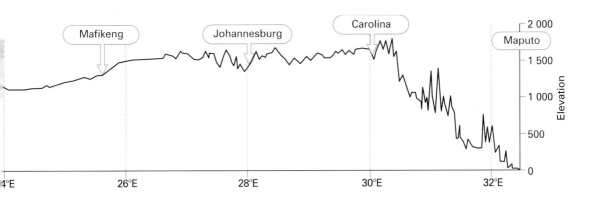

WHY IS THE DRAINAGE NETWORK OF SOUTHERN AFRICA SO ASYMMETRICAL?

The drainage of southern Africa is very asymmetrical. The Vaal and Orange rivers rise almost on the eastern escarpment, and then flow westward across the entire country to discharge into the Atlantic Ocean. By contrast, the Zambezi River system rises near the Atlantic coast and flows eastwards across the continent to the Indian Ocean. Almost all other easterly flowing rivers are much shorter, however, with the exception of the Limpopo. This asymmetry has its roots deep in the past, and to understand it, we need to delve back into the ancient history of these rivers.

The Limpopo River of today is but a small vestige of what it used to be. In the Cretaceous Period over 65 million years ago, its tributaries included the upper Zambezi, Kafue and Okavango rivers, and it provided the main drainage for southern central Africa. It is for this reason that the Limpopo River Delta, which extends from Maputo to Beira, is the largest on the African continent. At that time, the ancestral Orange-Vaal River, known as the Karoo River, discharged into the Atlantic Ocean much further south than it does today, probably via the Olifants River; and what is today the lower Orange River was part of a separate river system known as the Kalahari River. There were thus three major drainage systems in southern Africa. These were the Karoo (Orange-Vaal) and Kalahari rivers in the south, rising in the east and flowing west to the Atlantic; and further north, the ancestral Limpopo, rising almost on the west coast and flowing eastwards across the continent to the Indian Ocean.

This drainage pattern is believed to have been imprinted on the region when the supercontinent Gondwana broke up. Africa formed the core of Gondwana and was flanked in the east by Antarctica and in the west by South America. Breakup was caused by plumes of hot material that rose from deep in the Earth's mantle and then spread sideways like a mushroom beneath the cooler upper mantle and crust, causing them to bulge upwards. Plume bulges are huge, rising hundreds of metres and spreading to 2 000 km in diameter. Under such forces, the crust above the plume tears and slides apart under the influence of gravity, usually forming three rift valleys arranged at about 120° to each other and known as a triple junction. Such rift valleys usually widen and eventually become oceans when inundated. Sometimes, one of the rift branches may fail and does not progress beyond the valley stage, as is the situation around the plume at the southern end of the Red Sea. Here, two branches have opened to the ocean to create the Gulf of Aden and the Red Sea, while

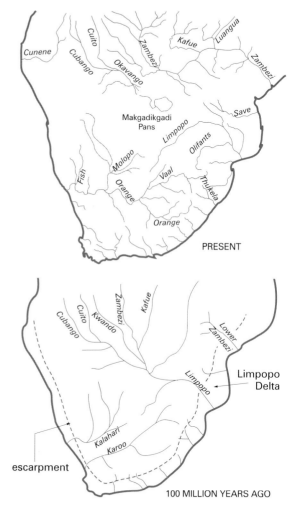

The major drainages of southern Africa as they are today (top) and as they were during the Cretaceous Period about 100 million years ago (above).

one branch is probably failing and remains in the rift valley stage, forming the East African Rift Valley. Later, and because the bulge remains elevated after rifting, radial river drainage patterns become established.

The Lebombo-Limpopo plume that initiated opening of the Indian Ocean was centred at the northern end of the Lebombo Mountains near Pafuri, where rifting started about 140 million years ago. Two branches opened that separated Antarctica from Africa, but the third branch lying along the current Limpopo valley never progressed beyond the rift valley stage. Elevated ground on the southwestern flank of the plume gave rise to westerly flowing rivers, which became the Karoo River system. But at that time, a high mountain range lay along the southern margin of South Africa, of which the Cape Mountains are a remnant, so the Karoo River skirted its northern flank and collected its tributaries, before emptying into the Atlantic.

The centre of the Parana-Etendeka plume that initiated opening of the Atlantic lay close to the current Cunene River mouth, where rifting commenced about 120 million years ago. Here, only two branches developed, along which South America and Africa separated. The associated bulge gave rise to easterly flowing rivers including the Omatako, Cubango, Cuito, Kwando and the western tributaries of the Zambezi. These rivers flowed eastwards into the rift valley formed by the Limpopo branch of the Lebombo-Limpopo plume. The Kalahari River drained the southern margin of the Parana-Etendeka plume and is today represented by the lower Orange, Kainab, Fish and Hartbees rivers and the Molopo River and its tributaries such as the Auob and Nossob.

These ancient river systems have undergone substantial adjustments since the Cretaceous Period as a result of erosion and geological processes that buckled and continue to rift and fracture the crust (see page 86), but the original asymmetry implanted at the time of breakup of Gondwana is still evident. Most notable is the southward propagation of the East African Rift Valley system, which has disrupted the upper tributaries of the ancestral Limpopo River and diverted some into the lower Zambezi River.

Africa was separated from Gondwana by the Lebombo-Limpopo plume, which opened the Indian Ocean; and the Parana-Etendeka plume, which opened the Atlantic Ocean.

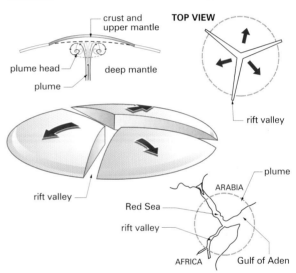

Rising mantle plumes cause the crust to bulge and split into three rifts, which may widen into oceans, such as the Red Sea-Gulf of Aden-East African Rift Valley split.

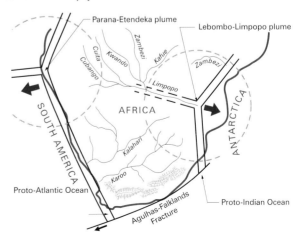

The mantle plumes that caused the opening of the Indian and Atlantic oceans also caused southern Africa's asymmetric drainage pattern.

WHY ARE SOME ROCK STRATA INCLINED WHEN OTHERS ARE HORIZONTAL?

Terence McCarthy

The Magaliesberg range, which extends from Pretoria to Rustenburg, is formed by a layer of sedimentary rock called quartzite that is inclined to the north at an angle of about 20°. Quartzite was formed by the deposition of very pure, hard and chemically resistant quartz sand in a shallow sea about 2 400 million years ago. Due to heat and pressure experienced by the sand after deposition, the grains more or less fused together, forming sandstone first, which on further heating became quartzite. Above and below the quartzite are layers of more easily weathered and eroded shale rocks, formed from compacted and heated mud and silt. The quartzite layer is much more extensive than the Magaliesberg range itself, and can be traced along arcs extending from Pretoria to Botswana and back to Thabazimbi, and from Carolina northwards to the Olifants River.

The Magaliesberg quartzite forms part of a pile of sedimentary strata deposited between 2 600 and

2 100 million years ago, when the region sank below sea level. A variety of horizontal sedimentary strata about 5 km thick were laid down during that event, the most important being dolomite, shale and quartzite, which are collectively known as the Transvaal Supergroup. About 2 061 million years ago, however, a vast quantity of molten rock (magma) from deep in the Earth's mantle was injected into the pile just above the level of the Magaliesberg quartzite. The magma spread laterally, forming a sheet of more than 120 000 km² that steadily thickened to about 8 km with further injections of molten material.

This layer is known as the Bushveld Complex and hosts the country's vast chromium, platinum and vanadium resources. The rocks have an average density of about 3 g/cm³, which weighs

GEOLOGICAL STRUCTURE OF THE MAGALIESBERG

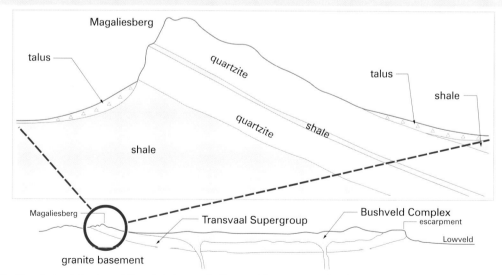

The Magaliesberg's hard quartzite rocks belong to the Transvaal Supergroup and preferential erosion of softer shales created its ridge. Intrusion of dense Bushveld Complex rocks onto part of the Transvaal Supergroup caused strata to sink and tilt locally.

The Magaliesberg range is formed by a layer of hard quartzite sedimentary rock, underlain and overlain by more easily eroded shales. The layers dip northwards at about 20° from the horizontal.

heavily on the less dense underlying Magaliesberg Formation (2.7 g/cm^3), causing it to sag into a dish-like shape, thus deforming the previously horizontally layered rocks so that they dip towards the centre of the depression.

Erosion has cut down through these various rocks, exposing the different layers. The surface expression of the layers varies depending on their hardness and chemical resistance. As quartzite is mechanically and chemically resistant, it forms ridges, whereas shale and dolomite are more easily weathered and eroded, so generally form lower, flatter topography, both of which give the Magaliesberg its characteristic profile. On the north side of the range, the shale has been completely removed leaving just the quartzite, whose inclination determines the dip of the land surface. On the south side, weathering and erosion of the softer shale undermines the hard quartzite layer, which breaks away along natural vertical cracks to produce steep cliffs. Scree slopes at the foot of the cliffs come from collapse of quartzite overhangs.

The Waterberg is composed mainly of horizontal quartzite layers deposited about 1 800 million years ago on vast river plains that received water and sediment from a mountain range to the north. There was no terrestrial vegetation at that time, so erosion was rapid and rivers flowed in multiple channels on laterally extensive sandy braid plains. This period was marked by the first appearance of free oxygen in the Earth's atmosphere, so iron in the rock is present as its red oxidized (ferric) form, colouring the rocks red. The Waterberg quartzite layers remain in more or less horizontal layers because there have been no subsequent geological events to disturb them. However, the Waterberg table-lands have been dissected by rivers, resulting in impressive gorges such as those north of Middelburg in Mpumalanga.

Horizontally layered rocks of the younger Karoo Supergroup were deposited between 300 and 180 million years ago across much of the interior of South Africa. They consist of a variety of sedimentary rocks, including glacial deposits, deep- and shallow-water mudstones, siltstones and sandstones. About 180 million years ago, vast amounts of molten rock from deep in the Earth's mantle intruded into the Karoo sedimentary strata. Some spread laterally, forming horizontal sills of dolerite, while the rest intruded through to the surface, erupting as voluminous lava flows that formed a layer almost 2 km thick.

As there has been very little geological disturbance of the Karoo Supergroup, horizontal layering of the Karoo strata is still clearly evident, especially in the Drakensberg, where erosion has caused considerable vertical relief. Similarly, the iconic flat-topped Karoo koppies have been little disturbed. Their hard dolerite caps (or lava in the case of Harrismith Mountain) protect the underlying soft sedimentary rock from erosion, while the overlying material has been removed completely.

Getaway / D. Steele / Digital Source

Terence McCarthy

Sedimentary rocks and lava flows form roughly horizontal layers, as evident in the 1 800 million-year-old Waterberg strata (left) and the 180 million-year-old rocks of Harrismith Mountain (right). They remain so unless disturbed by later earth movements.

6 | LIFE

WHEN DID LIFE FIRST APPEAR ON EARTH?

What are the essential requirements for life? From a human perspective, the answer is an environment that is neither too hot nor too cold (about 5°C to 35°C), and one that has water, organic food to eat and oxygen to breathe. But humans are not alone on Earth, and other organisms have different yardsticks. Organisms have been found living in water pockets in polar ice at -40°C, and can certainly survive even lower temperatures. At the other extreme, some organisms can survive at over 130°C. Liquid water is essential for both these extremes, whether hot or cold – a situation that occurs under very high pressure, when both the boiling and freezing points of water are raised or lowered, respectively. As for food, organic material is only one of many substances organisms use to obtain energy. Others include gases such as hydrogen, sulphur dioxide, hydrogen sulphide and methane, as well as solids such as rust, sulphur, metallic iron and many others. Breathing oxygen is essential for most animals, but for many organisms oxygen is not required and may even be toxic. Additionally, some organisms can happily tolerate hypersaline water, extreme pressure or even close proximity to highly radioactive materials.

The only critical requirements for life on Earth are appropriate temperature (particularly the upper limit), the presence of water and some sort of food resource. On early Earth, carbon compounds and potential chemical foodstuffs were abundant, so when did Earth become habitable and life first appear?

The Earth formed around 4 540 million years ago in a hot cloud of gas and dust (see page 12), growing as planetesimal bodies clumped together to enlarge the nascent planet. Some bodies were large and their collisions with Earth produced sufficient heat to melt it, while one collision 4 530 million years ago by a Mars-sized object formed the Moon (see

Stromatolites of calcium carbonate were formed in the oceans by photosynthetic bacteria as early as 3 200 million years ago, as revealed in these rocks from Barberton.

The oldest known sedimentary rock on Earth is the 3 800 million-year-old Isua iron formation in Greenland. Carbon associated with these rocks has an isotopic signature indicating that it originated from living organisms.

page 20). At that stage, Earth had no liquid water, but evidence suggests that surface water may have appeared 4 400 million years ago as Earth cooled, making it potentially habitable, despite still frequent impacts. These intensified about 3 900 million years ago during the Late Bombardment period, when any oceans were probably vaporized. It is even suggested that sufficient heat was generated to sterilize Earth, so that perhaps life appeared only after the Late Bombardment when water reappeared. Evidence for this appears in the oldest known water-lain sedimentary rocks from 3 800 million years ago.

What traces of early life might we recognize today? Early organisms would certainly have been single celled and mostly without hard body parts to fossilize. Even so, silica replicas of single-celled organisms have been found in 3 500 million-year-old sedimentary deposits from the Barberton region. Another trace of early life has been found in the form of microscopic etchings in volcanic glass produced by certain bacteria in their quest for nutrients. These tube-like structures have been well documented in modern volcanic rocks from ocean floors, while identical structures have been found in 3 450 million-year-old volcanic rocks from Barberton. Life was therefore well established on Earth by 3 400 million years ago, despite occasional extraterrestrial impacts.

Chemical signatures provide other clues of early life. Carbon is the essential component of living things, and is composed primarily of the non-radioactive ^{13}C and ^{12}C isotopes, the former being heavier than the latter due to its greater atomic mass (13). Significantly, lighter isotopes can pass through cell walls more easily than heavier isotopes. Thus, carbon fixation by photosynthesis separates the carbon isotopes in such a way that ^{12}C atoms are more abundant in photosynthesizers than ^{13}C atoms, so that deposits containing predominantly the lighter isotope provide evidence for photosynthesis. Carbon-bearing, 3 800 million-year-old sedimentary deposits in Greenland show exactly this, and provide evidence of the earliest life thus far discovered, most probably photosynthetic cyanobacteria.

If the Late Bombardment sterilized Earth 3 900 million years ago, this implies that photosynthesizing species evolved in no more than 100 million years. Even single prokaryotic cells are immensely sophisticated systems, and it seems inconceivable that their evolution took so short a time, particularly since life does not appear to have evolved much over the next 2 000 million years (see 148). There are several possible explanations for the puzzlingly rapid appearance of life on Earth: (1) life is ancient and widespread throughout the Universe and was delivered to Earth by comets; (2) life arose on another planet (possibly Mars) and was delivered to Earth after the Late Bombardment in fragments of (Martian) rock blasted into space; (3) life developed on Earth before the Late Bombardment and some forms survived in rocks deep below Earth's surface, thus escaping the sterilization event; (4) the Earth's surface was not sterilized at all by the Late Bombardment. As yet, the apparently rapid appearance of life on Earth remains a mystery that requires further study of Earth's most ancient rocks, as well as a search for life in the Solar System and especially the current thrust to seek evidence for life on Mars.

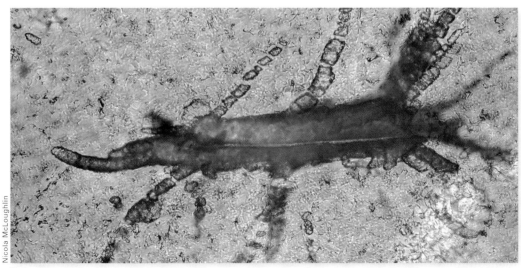

Nicola McLoughlin

Etch structures in volcanic glass in 3 450 million-year-old lavas from Barberton indicate that life was well established on Earth by that time.

HAS THE DIVERSITY AND COMPLEXITY OF LIFE CHANGED OVER TIME?

Earth's earliest life forms may still exist today, such as these slimy coatings of heat-loving bacteria living around hot springs at Yellowstone National Park, USA.

Fossilized bones and shells first appeared in rocks about 545 million years ago and reveal the nature and chronological development of life since then. However, complex soft-bodied life forms originated perhaps 100 million years earlier, but are known only by rare body impressions or tracks. Yet older rocks, representing much of Earth's 4 500 million-year history, contain very few traces of life. To shed light on those traces, geneticists and biologists have now turned to molecular tools and the study of primitive microorganisms to further unravel the origins of life.

All living organisms consist of cells containing the chemicals of life, wrapped in a cell membrane. All make use of the same four DNA nucleotide chains to store the instructions for replicating the organism, while simpler RNA nucleotide chains read the DNA code and carry out its instructions. Additionally, all use amino acids and sugars in their metabolism. These three classes of molecules come in left- and right-handed versions (like gloves), and all organisms show the same selectivity for left- or right-handed forms. Finally, genetic studies reveal that all species have certain genes in common. With such cellular commonality, the inescapable conclusion is that all living things arose from a common ancestor, named LUCA – the last universal common ancestor. We don't know exactly what LUCA was like, but the simplest organisms known are bacteria and their kin, and it is here that the search for LUCA is focused.

Molecular studies on RNA from single-celled, bacteria-like organisms without nuclei (prokaryotes) show that they fall into the eubacteria or the more primitive archaea. Amongst the latter, extreme heat-loving varieties appear closest to the rootstock of life, and probably lived in hot springs using hydrogen sulphide and dissolved iron as an energy source (see pages 8 and 10). The diversity and complexity of life we find today arose from these humble ancestors. Remarkably, organisms apparently very similar to these still exist around volcanic hot springs, like living fossils, contributing to life's immense diversity and also providing living relics for study.

As life diversified, all forms remained exclusively aquatic and adapted to the oxygen-free environment. A significant early development was the appearance of photosynthetic cyanobacteria, which synthesized organic carbon from carbon dioxide and produced oxygen as a waste product, using sunlight as an energy source. They appeared about 3 800 million years ago and dominated early Earth, leaving their signature as characteristic fossil accretionary, stromatolite structures. Cyanobacteria still exist today, apparently unchanged over the past 3 400 million years.

The earliest fish were jawless, such as this ancient species found fossilized in South Africa.

A significant evolutionary step was the appearance in the oceans of photosynthetic bacteria, which still exist today. They form characteristic stromatolites, such as these at Shark Bay in Western Australia.

Cyanobacteria had a profound effect on Earth. They changed the composition of the carbon dioxide-dominated atmosphere to one dominated by nitrogen and oxygen, which at that time was toxic to most life forms (see page 54). This change heralded new eukaryote life forms between 1 800 and 1 500 million years ago, which had cells with nuclei and organelles to cope with the highly reactive oxygenated atmosphere. Eukaryotes resulted from a symbiosis between species of archaea and eubacteria. One species formed the host cell, another the cell nucleus, and a third the mitochondria, where cellular metabolism takes place. These cells became the ancestors of all animals. A separate symbiotic association led to the incorporation of cyanobacteria into cells to form chloroplasts, where photosynthesis takes place, which became the ancestors of all plants.

As the oxygen content in the atmosphere rose due to photosynthesis, cells could form cellular colonies still able to obtain oxygen by diffusion. Today's sponges and seaweeds represent this stage in life's history. In the interval from 1 100 to 600 million years ago, cells took on different tasks in such colonies, laying the foundation for modern organisms. By 600 million years ago (the Ediacaran Period), the soft-bodied ancestors of all of today's major animal groups (phyla) had appeared. Then, quite suddenly 545 million years ago, organisms with hard body parts appeared and rapidly increased in number during the Cambrian Explosion, when diversification of life continued apace.

In the oceans, the first fish arose 450 to 500 million years ago, leading to lobe-finned fish like the coelacanth. Amphibians appeared 370 million years ago, opening up the colonization of land by animals. The land was not entirely barren, as waxy-coated algae had become terrestrial by 430 million years ago, and were followed by insects 10 million years later. From these early beginnings, terrestrial life developed rapidly and, by 350 million years ago, great forests populated by reptiles dominated the landscape. The full diversity of terrestrial organisms

The lobe-finned coelacanth ultimately provided the rootstock of all terrestrial animals.

is unknown, however, because of the limitations of fossilization. However, many marine animals are readily fossilized and provide the best measure of marine diversity. They indicate a rapid increase in diversity from 545 to 438 million years ago, followed by a long period of slowly declining diversity, culminating in the end-Permian mass extinction event 248 million years ago. Thereafter, the diversity and complexity of marine life steadily rose, although punctuated by later extinction events (see page 156), and today is greater than ever before.

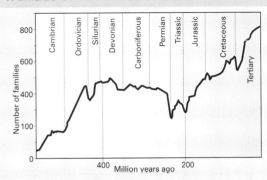

FAMILIES OF MARINE ORGANISMS OVER TIME

The number of families of marine animals provides one measure of the diversity of marine organisms, which is currently greater than ever before.

WHAT ARE FOSSILS?

A fossil is a relic of a once-living organism preserved in rock. Only a very small proportion of living things become fossilized, and some organisms are more likely to become fossilized than others, such as those with hard body parts, especially if they live in water. In contrast, land-dwelling, soft, fleshy organisms are very seldom fossilized. There are many different ways in which dead organisms can be preserved, so fossils are very diverse in their make-up.

Other than these 'body fossils', there are also 'trace fossils', not of the organisms themselves, but impressions left by the activities of organisms during their lifetime. Examples of such relics include sand- or mud-filled burrows, tracks, living structures such as termite mounds, and stromatolites, formed when living cyanobacteria accumulated calcium carbonate that was subsequently preserved. Stromatolites are the most widespread relic of early life on Earth. The easiest way to grasp body fossil diversity is to examine the many processes leading to fossil formation.

Henia Czekanowska

Tree gum, which on burial becomes the mineral amber, may encapsulate insects and so preserve them.

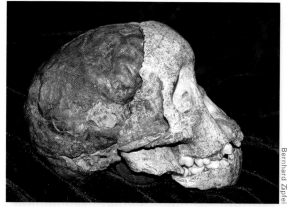

Bernhard Zipfel

The cranium of the famous Taung skull has broken away, revealing a cast of the brain on which convolutions and even blood vessels are clearly visible.

Entombed in amber: Some species of trees, such as pine trees, exude sticky gum when the bark is damaged. Insects alighting on the gum become trapped and may become entombed by further exudates of gum. When buried in sediment under suitable conditions, the gum undergoes a hardening polymerization process and is converted to a yellow, transparent, natural form of plastic known as amber. The process does no damage to entombed insects. Amber is a sought-after semiprecious stone used in jewellery, and the presence of entombed insects adds greatly to its value.

Soft tissue preservation: Organisms consisting of soft tissue do not readily become fossilized. However, if buried rapidly in material capable of forming a hard shell, the organism will decay, leaving a cavity having its exact shape. This is known as a mould, and is a negative of the original form. Moulds of humans were formed in this way by volcanic ash when Mt Vesuvius erupted in 79 AD, destroying the city of Pompeii. The voids were discovered during the archaeological excavation of the city, and were filled with plaster and then excavated from the surrounding volcanic ash to reveal the death agonies of the victims. More commonly, moulds formed by soft tissue become filled with material some time after formation, such as very fine, muddy material or a chemical precipitate like calcium carbonate, producing a solid replica or cast of the original form. Faeces are quite commonly preserved in this way, and are known as coprolites or 'dung stones'. Even casts of brains have been found, a notable example being that of the famous Taung Child.

Impressions and carbonization: Leaves, flowers or insects falling into muddy water become buried in sediment and over time are flattened and compacted as more sediment is deposited on top of them. The original organism may decay completely, and all that is left is an impression, which appears if the rock is broken open in the correct orientation. The impression may be enhanced by a thin layer of mineral matter such as the orange-brown iron oxide, hematite. Sometimes, the organism does not decay completely, but undergoes chemical changes involving the loss of water and hydrogen from the tissue, leaving a residue of carbon. If the host rock is broken in the correct orientation, an impression of the organism will be seen coated with carbon, or simply as a carbon image of the organism. Coal is formed in much the same way from plant material.

Preservation of original hard parts of organisms: The hard body parts of organisms may be preserved in their original form after burial in sediment. This often occurs with shells, and less commonly with teeth and bones. This phenomenon is relatively common in geologically more recent fossilized material.

Replacement: Hard body parts often become chemically replaced by a secondary mineral after burial in sediment. Geologically older fossils are generally found replaced in this way. The process seems to occur slowly, almost molecule by molecule, so that delicate, even microscopic structures of the original are preserved. A variety of minerals can replace the original material, including calcium carbonate (calcite or aragonite), silica, pyrite (iron sulphide), hematite (iron oxide) and apatite (calcium phosphate).

Permineralization: This is a process whereby water-filled cavities in an organism, such as the interior of plant cells, become filled with mineral matter, commonly silica. Like replacement, this process is probably very slow, and often leads to perfect preservation of the cellular structure of plant material. When it occurs more rapidly, only the macroscopic features of the original object are preserved.

Molluscs are commonly found as fossils because their shells are readily incorporated in sediment.

Animals may be fossilized if they die in situations where their bones are buried in sediment.

Trace fossils are structures or tracks left by an organism, rather than the organism itself, such as these columns near Mapungubwe which are 250 million-year-old fossil termite mounds.

HOW SECURE IS DARWIN'S THEORY OF EVOLUTION?

Darwin's 1859 theory for the origin of the diversity of living organisms, published in his seminal book *On the Origin of Species*, met with very mixed reactions from his peers. On palaeontological grounds, his arguments appeared weak because the fossil record then was very sparse. Those fossils that did exist appeared to suggest that a great diversity of life forms suddenly appeared all at once, fully developed, as if there had been a sudden act of creation. Darwin's idea that every one of these early species arose from some ancestral form had to be largely accepted on faith, because no ancestral fossil forms were then known. Even later fossil species seemed to appear fully developed, apparently without any evidence of intermediate or ancestral fossil forms.

The situation has, however, changed radically since that time. We now know that the sudden appearance of diverse fossilized animals 540 million years ago in what is known as the Cambrian Explosion simply reflects the widespread adoption of hard body parts. Prior to then, all animals had only soft body parts, which are seldom well fossilized. We know, too, that life abounded in the oceans before the appearance of hard-bodied organisms, exactly as Darwin had surmised.

Darwin predicted that intermediate fossil forms would be found to link the major animal and plant genera in their respective ancestral lineages. He has been proven correct, and we now have an excellent fossil record of the development of complex life forms. These include links from sea urchins to fish to amphibians to reptiles and finally to mammals. Although we can see the overall picture clearly, there are nevertheless gaps in the fossil record between successive groups of species. In some cases however, the record of gradual transition via a series of intermediate forms is almost complete, as in the transition from reptiles to mammals. Fossils from rocks of the Karoo Supergroup in South Africa

reveal an almost continuous record of increasingly mammal-like features from 250 to 180 million years ago that belong to mammal-like reptiles, or therapsids. These features involve closing of the palate and rearrangement of the jaw bones to form a single jaw bone and bones in the inner ear.

Embryonic development also supports the notion of evolution because, as embryos develop,

SIMILARITIES IN THE BONE STRUCTURE OF VERTEBRATE LIMBS

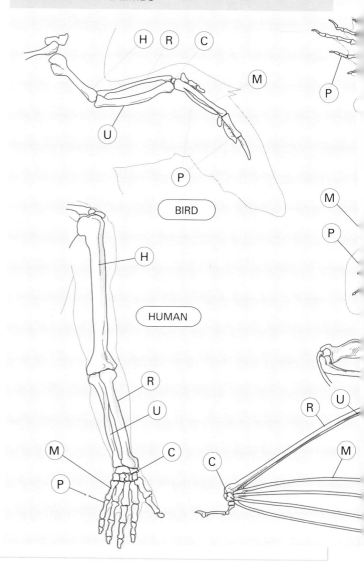

BIRD

HUMAN

they recognizably pass through the evolutionary stages of that particular species, although in a very general way. The human foetus, for example, begins as a single cell that grows into a hollow sphere, which then inwardly folds to form a two-layered cup-like structure similar to jellyfish and their kin. Next, the foetus elongates and appears to pass through stages involving gills, a tail and fin-like limbs such as in lobe-finned fish and amphibians, eventually taking on mammal-like characteristics. Only after two months does the developing embryo resemble a primate. Relatively rare incomplete embryonic development can produce birth defects that point to our ancestral evolutionary stages. For example, human babies are occasionally born with gill slits, reflecting our early evolution from fish, or more commonly with a cleft palate, reflecting our distant reptilian ancestry.

Molecular genetics has also provided powerful support for evolutionary theory, showing that all animals have certain genes in common, and that similar species share more genes in common. Thus humans and chimpanzees have about 98% of their genes in common, indicating close ancestral ties. But even apparently unrelated species have some genes in common, while also sharing more or less obvious commonalities. For example, animals as diverse as crocodiles, dogs, birds and humans all have the same basic bone structure, reflecting their common ancestry.

Darwin developed the notion that evolution was driven by competition and natural selection ('survival of the fittest') that arose from diversity within a species. Remarkably, he devised his theory when genetics was unknown. Much later, the discovery of genes and genetic coding has validated his ideas by providing an understanding of the origins of diversity within a species and how particular traits may arise and be passed on to successive generations. Moreover, we have witnessed the efficacy of genetic diversity and natural selection in action in several unintended large-scale experiments. For example, some rats have developed immunity to the common rat poison 'warfarin', while chloroquin-resistant malaria has appeared alongside drug-resistant TB. All arise from rare genetic mutations that allowed these individuals to multiply and even become the dominant form. Lessons learnt from this are now routinely applied in medicine, such as in TB and AIDS treatment. Instead of a single drug or antibiotic, a cocktail of different drugs is routinely used to reduce the risk of immune individuals arising, which then render individual drugs ineffective.

When Darwin first proposed the idea of evolution, he had to make many assumptions, of which most are now vindicated. So although we still talk of evolutionary theory, the overwhelming evidence supports it as fact rather than theory.

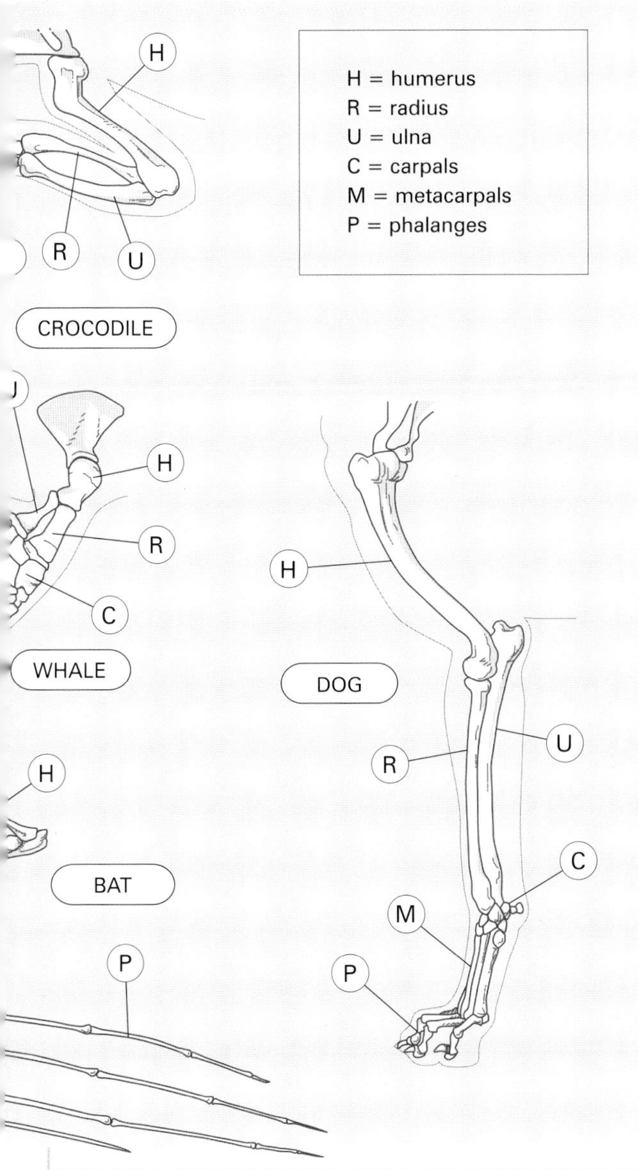

H = humerus
R = radius
U = ulna
C = carpals
M = metacarpals
P = phalanges

CROCODILE

WHALE

DOG

BAT

All vertebrates have a similar bone structure, illustrated here by similarities of the arm/forelimb/wing of a human, a bat, a dog, a crocodile, a bird and a whale, indicating their common ancestry.

FROM WHERE DID HUMANS ORIGINATE?

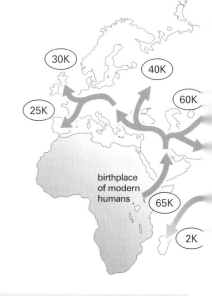

This question forms the core of an important debate in palaeoanthropology that has raged over the past two decades or so, often referred to as the Out-of-Africa model versus the Multiregional model – i.e. an exclusively African origin for mankind, or parallel evolution in different parts of the world. Evidence that fuels the debate comes from the study of fossil bones and teeth, artifacts (stone tools and the like) and from the genetic characteristics of modern peoples, and very rarely from excavated bones.

There is general consensus that early humans originated in Africa because our closest relatives (gorillas, bonobos and chimpanzees) are found only in Africa and fossils of ancient human ancestors are also restricted to Africa. Thus, the early part of the human evolutionary tree is populated entirely by African species dating back about 7 million years ago to *Sahelanthropus tchadensis*. There was considerable diversity amongst these early ancestors and several different species coexisted at any one time, making construction of a complete evolutionary tree very difficult. The first species of *Homo* appeared in Africa about 2.5 million years ago, named *Homo habilis* ('handy man') because of its ability to manufacture crude stone tools. About 1.7 million years ago, *Homo erectus* emerged, characterized by large body size (about 1.8 m tall) and a powerful build. This species may have arisen via the earlier *Homo ergaster*, although the exact status of this latter species is uncertain. Not only was *Homo erectus* more robust than any of its predecessors, it was also a lot smarter, being the first to control fire and able to manufacture large, symmetrically-shaped hand axes, known as Acheulian tools. *Homo erectus* was also a traveller, and soon spread beyond Africa into Europe

Terence McCarthy

Throughout Africa, Europe and Asia, *Homo erectus* made the iconic large hand axes known as Acheulian tools between 1.4 million and 200 000 years ago.

THE DISPERSAL OF HUMANS AROUND THE WORLD

The spread of modern humans, *Homo sapiens sapiens*, around the globe has been deciphered from genetic studies of humankind.

and Asia, laying the foundations for the multiregional hypothesis of human origins. Proponents of this argue that our species, *Homo sapiens*, evolved simultaneously across Europe and Asia from a founding population of *Homo erectus* to form the different races of today.

The alternative view is that a new species, a primitive or archaic form of *Homo sapiens*, evolved in Africa from *Homo erectus*. Amongst these archaic forms were *Homo rhodesiensis*, *Homo heidelbergensis* and *Homo antecessor*, the oldest archaic form known. Archaic *Homo* also migrated out of Africa into Europe, giving rise to the Neanderthals, *Homo neanderthalensis*, who dominated in Europe from about 500 000 years ago, evidently displacing *Homo erectus*. The fortunes of these species in Europe and Asia waxed and waned with the Ice Ages that characterized the past 2 million years. During these events, great ice sheets advanced across northern Europe and Asia displacing all before them. Neanderthals seemed to have been quite adept at living in these frigid conditions, but the *Homo erectus* line petered out.

The Out-of-Africa model argues that modern humans (*Homo sapiens sapiens*) evolved relatively recently from archaic *Homo sapiens* somewhere in Africa

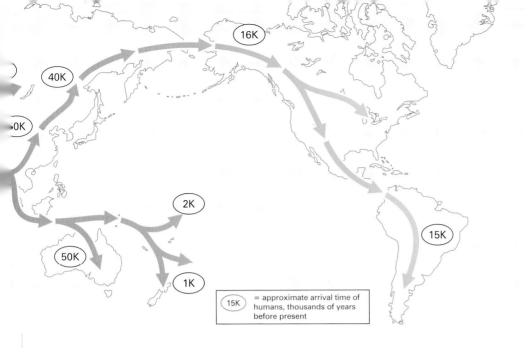

around 200 000 years ago. The oldest anatomically modern humans found so far are from Ethopia, and date to 190 000 years ago, followed by specimens from Klasies River mouth in South Africa (115 000 years old). Cultural modernity, signified by the use of ochre for personal adornment and shell beads, seems to have appeared in modern humans about 80 000 to 100 000 years ago. These culturally modern people evidently displaced archaic forms in Africa and became the sole representatives of *Homo*. The San (Bushman) people of southern Africa show the greatest genetic diversity of all human groups, indicating that they are genetically closest to this ancient rootstock of humanity.

Genetic evidence supports the view that modern humans appeared suddenly outside Africa about 60 000 years ago, reflecting a third wave of *Homo* emigration from the continent that spread rapidly around the globe. Migration was probably greatly facilitated by the last Ice Age, which commenced about 80 000 years ago and lasted until about 12 000 years ago, albeit with variations in the extent of ice cover. Expansion of the ice caps during the last glacial maximum 18 000 years ago resulted in a 130 m fall in sea level. This created land bridges between many previously separated land masses, such as between Europe, Great Britain and Ireland and between the Indonesian islands, thus greatly facilitating colonization. The original émigrés were probably few in number, but with their language and technology they were readily able to adapt to the diverse conditions encountered, so they multiplied rapidly. Expansion was rapid across southern Asia and south into

Australasia, which was accomplished about 50 000 years ago, roughly 10 000 years after their initial departure from Africa. Europe was colonized only about 40 000 years ago. *Homo sapiens sapiens* coexisted with *Homo neanderthalensis* in Europe from about 40 000 years ago, and a bit earlier in the Middle East, but following the arrival of modern humans, the Neanderthals declined in numbers and eventually became extinct about 28 000 years ago. The most rapid spread of humanity was across the Americas, accomplished in just 1 000 years following their crossing from Asia 16 000 years ago. Island outposts in the Indian and Pacific oceans were colonized only in the last few thousand years, completing the current global spread of humanity.

THE FAMILY TREE AND GEOGRAPHICAL SPREAD OF HUMANKIND

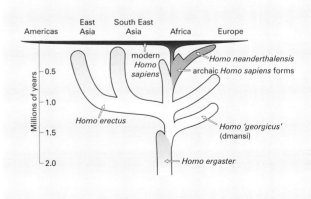

WHAT CAUSED MASS EXTINCTIONS?

Animals with hard body parts first appeared on Earth about 550 million years ago (see page 148) and since then have diversified into the wide range of organisms we find today. The fossil record shows, however, that this evolutionary road has been rocky, and that about 99% of species that ever lived have become extinct. Species came and went in the relentless competition of life, giving rise to a natural though slow background extinction rate. Every now and then, however, this progression was punctuated by mass extinctions, when vast numbers of species simultaneously became extinct. The most famous of these was the extinction of the dinosaurs at the end of the Cretaceous Period,

65 million years ago. The effect of such mass extinctions was so globally pervasive and distinctive that they have been used to subdivide the geological time scale.

Mass extinctions probably occurred over periods of tens to hundreds of thousands of years and simultaneously and globally affected a wide variety of terrestrial and marine organisms, although some groups survived unscathed. The extinction of the dinosaurs was just one of about 30 mass extinction events of which we are aware. Of these, five were catastrophic and are listed in the table below, with their severity measured in terms of marine species and families lost. These are known as the 'Big Five mass extinctions'.

The simultaneous global extinction of many different, unrelated species can only be due to a breakdown in the global ecosystem, but what could have caused this? Many different mechanisms have been proposed, and here the most prominent are explored.

An impact from space: The impact of a large comet or asteroid could have catastrophic effects on global ecosystems. Most importantly, it would blast a huge quantity of dust into the atmosphere, blotting out the Sun for months or even years. This theory proposes that the subsequent fall in temperature and absence of sunlight would result in global cooling and die-off of most vegetation. As plants support the global food chain, including both terrestrial and marine animals, many lineages would die out. But if so, what evidence of this should we look for? Impacts by asteroids or comets leave unique chemical fingerprints, such as the metal iridium, and they also blast out shock-damaged minerals that are uniquely diagnostic.

A nearby stellar explosion or gamma-ray burst: Some stars end their lives in spectacular explosions known as supernovae. These events produce a relatively short-lived, but extremely intense burst of radiation in the form of gamma and x-rays. There are also other events of uncertain origin that produce intense bursts of gamma rays (called GRBs). If either of

MAJOR EXTINCTION EVENTS

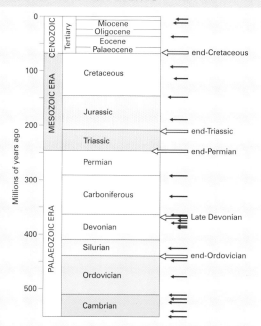

Mass extinctions have a huge effect on the number of **species** (see table below), but at the level of **families**, the effect is less severe, as a few representatives of most orders invariably manage to survive.

EXTINCTION	PERIOD TIME (millions of years)	MARINE SPP. LOST (%)	FAMILIES LOST (%)
1. Ordovician	440	85	20
2. Devonian	354	80	19
3. Permian	245	96	53
4. Triassic	210	76	20
5. Cretaceous	65	75	17

Note: Marine organisms are used as an index of extinction events because they are readily fossilized.

Dinosaurs were one of the most successful animal lineages of all time, and were global in their distribution. They included species such as *Coelophysis (Syntarsus) rhodesiensis* from Zimbabwe, shown here. Dinosaurs were virtually wiped out 65 million years ago, although their descendants live on in the form of birds.

L. Penny

these events occurred within a few light years of the Earth, it is likely that the intensity of radiation would breach Earth's protective atmosphere, resulting in widespread death of organisms from radiation damage, except for deep-sea organisms and those living underground.

Volcanic eruptions: These are relatively localized events, and while they can be very destructive, even causing short-term climate change, they are typically unable to disrupt global ecosystems sufficiently to cause a mass extinction. However, a flood basalt volcanic eruption could be sufficiently intense to have a lasting global effect. These are relatively rare and are formed by plumes of material rising from deep in the Earth's mantle. What makes them special is the huge quantity and speed of lava eruption. One of the best studied is the Deccan Traps of western India, which covers about a third of the subcontinent and consists of lava flows totaling 2 000 m in thickness that erupted in less than 500 000 years about 65 million years ago. Huge amounts of sulphur dioxide and carbon dioxide were probably released along with the lava, producing sufficient acid rain on a global scale to perhaps poison surface waters. Carbon

dioxide would also induce global warming, heating the oceans and causing various other adverse effects discussed below.

Fall in sea level: A major fall in sea level exposes continental shelves, which can have a profound effect on marine life, as most biologically productive regions are in shallow shelf waters. Falls in sea level can be initiated by global cooling, which locks sea water into ice caps, but ice cover is of short duration and seems to have a limited effect on marine life. More significant are alterations in sea level due to changes in the configuration of tectonic plates, specifically the number and activity

EXTINCTIONS AND SEA LEVEL CHANGES

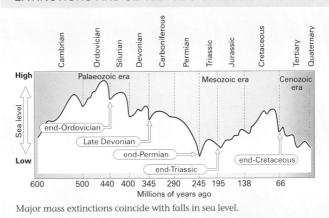

Major mass extinctions coincide with falls in sea level.

THE ATMOSPHERE AND GLOBAL CLIMATE OVER TIME

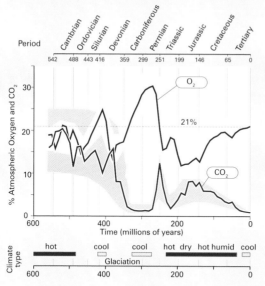

The oxygen and carbon dioxide contents of the atmosphere and global climate have changed over time, possibly contributing to mass extinction events.

The end of the Cretaceous is marked here by a distinct layer of rock that contains an elevated concentration of iridium and shocked quartz, both indicative of an impact by an extraterrestrial object.

of mid-ocean ridges, which can cause longer lasting rises or falls in sea level and sustained exposure or flooding of continental shelves, with profound effects on marine life.

Sustained global warming: Species adapted to cold conditions would be adversely affected, but more widespread effects could occur via ocean-atmosphere interactions. The solubility of gases in water decreases with increasing temperature, so as oceans warm, oxygen concentrations would decline and some marine organisms could be affected. If large-scale death and decay of these organisms took place, this would further deplete oxygen concentrations. Furthermore, cold, deep-ocean floor sediments contain clathrates, which are chemical combinations of gases such as methane and water. Warming of the oceans could destabilize these compounds, releasing large amounts of methane into the water column and the atmosphere. Methane oxidation would further deplete oxygen concentrations in the water, whilst its presence in the atmosphere would promote further global warming because methane is a greenhouse gas. Methane oxidation in the atmosphere would also deplete atmospheric oxygen, producing carbon dioxide, another greenhouse gas. Very low oxygen concentrations in the oceans would lead to hypoxia or anoxia and the growth of anaerobic bacteria that derive energy by converting sulphate to hydrogen sulphide, which is toxic to most oxygen breathers. Escape of large amounts of this gas into the atmosphere could cause widespread poisoning and also acid rain, affecting both marine and terrestrial species.

The end-Cretaceous mass extinction of the dinosaurs is widely considered to be due to the impact of an extraterrestrial object at Chicxulub in southern Mexico. This is the only extinction event for which strong evidence of an impact exists, namely the presence of the telltale iridium spike and shocked mineral grains in rocks deposited at the end of the Cretaceous Period. However, the impact alone could not have caused the extinction, as the similarly sized Popigai impact in Siberia is not associated with an extinction event. Instead, the target rocks at Chicxulub were rich in sulphur and carbon dioxide, so it appears that a combination of atmospheric dust and acid rain did the damage.

Even so, the end-Cretaceous extinction coincides with outpouring of the flood basalts that formed the Deccan Traps, which has been proposed as an alternative cause of this extinction due to the associated effects of acid rain and global warming. Supporting this theory is the fact that most mass extinction events over the last 300 million years, including three of the big five, coincided with flood basalt eruptions. So there is still no consensus on what killed the dinosaurs. Causes of the other four major extinction events are shrouded in even more uncertainty. Flood basalt eruptions are a strong candidate, but since all of the five major mass extinctions also coincide with abrupt falls in sea level, the latter could be implicated. However, separating cause and effect is complicated, because sea level falls may be related to flood basalt eruptions as both are linked to plate tectonic processes. Thus both processes may have worked together in contributing to mass extinctions. The scenario proposed for causing the end-Ordovician extinction is global cooling and sea level fall due to major glacial activity, known in South Africa as the Pakhuis glaciation. The end-Devonian event occurred in two stages and seems to have affected mainly marine organisms. Suggested causes for this include an asteroid impact (the Woodleigh crater in Western Australia), a fall in sea level, or possibly the development of hypoxia in the oceans. The

end-Permian mass extinction was the greatest of all and occurred in two stages separated by about 8 million years. Fish and certain bottom-dwelling species survived, but iconic species such as trilobites, most therapsids and glossopterids were wiped out. Amongst the survivors were the reptilian ancestors of dinosaurs and a single, mammal-like reptile species from which mammals arose. In addition to the eruption of massive flood basalt sequences of the Emeishan Traps of China and the Siberian Traps 8 million years later, the end-Permian extinction event coincided with widespread hypoxia in the oceans. The world was warming at the time and methane and hydrogen sulphide may have been released from sediments creating a potentially fatal oxygen-deficient environment. The end-Triassic extinction might be related to the impact of a swarm of comets that created the Manicougan and St Martin craters in Canada, the Rochechouart crater in France, and some smaller ones in the USA and Ukraine. Although there is some uncertainty about the relative timing of these impacts vis-à-vis the end-Triassic extinction, sea level also fell at this time, with potentially fatal consequences for many continental-shelf marine organisms.

EXTINCTION EVENTS AND MAJOR BASALT ERUPTIONS

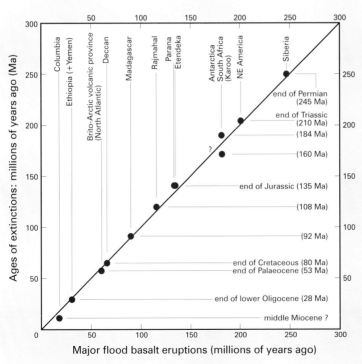

Most flood basalt events, which involved the rapid eruption of huge amounts of lava and the release of noxious gases, coincided with, and may have caused, many of the mass extinction events.

WHAT IS THE SIXTH EXTINCTION?

The fossil record reveals that species regularly become extinct, but shows also that this normally slow process has been punctuated by relatively abrupt mass extinction events. About 30 such extinctions have been recognized, but five were absolutely catastrophic, when more than 70% of all species became extinct. The last of these major events occurred 65 million years ago and ended the reign of dinosaurs on land and ammonites in the oceans. The causes of these extinction events remain a topic of research and debate (see page 156), but here we consider a much more recent event.

Palaeontologists studying the world's fauna of the last 100 000 years have found evidence for a recent mass extinction of a very unusual kind. It has selectively eliminated animals weighing more than about 50 kg – the megafauna – and it occurred in different regions of the globe at different times. Europe and northern Asia were hit between 40 000 and 13 000 years ago; Australia and New Guinea between 40 000 and 25 000 years ago; the Pacific Islands, including New Zealand, between 3 000 and 200 years ago; North and South America between 11 000 and 10 000 years ago; and Madagascar between 1 000 and 200 years ago. Africa was only mildly affected, and relatively few species of megafauna were lost. In contrast, Australia lost 46 species or 92% of its megafauna, while North America lost 57 species or 75% of its large mammals including elephants, mastodons, giant sloths, sabre-tooth cats, horses and camels. Today's larger North American species such as bison and elk are actually not indigenous, but arrived 13 000 years ago from Asia.

The past 2 million years, known as the Pleistocene Epoch, has been characterized by several Ice Ages in which the northern polar ice cap expanded over large areas of the northern continents. The last Ice Age ended about 12 000 years ago and initially scientists believed that megafaunal extinctions of the past 100 000 years were related to climatic disruption caused by the last of the Ice Ages, especially in North America. However, as information has emerged about the timing of human migration around the globe, the coincidence between human arrivals and megafaunal extinctions became clear (see page 154). Archaeological evidence shows that megafauna were severely overhunted, despite previous assumptions that hunting large animals was dangerous for early settlers using primarily spears, bows and arrows. Instead, megafauna of the time were probably unfamiliar with humans and unaware of the danger

Colin MacRae

Over the past 500 million years there have been five major mass extinction events. One such event claimed the ammonites, which dominated Cretaceous seas.

David McCarthy

In modern times, the major cause of extinctions of larger animals such as giant tortoises (right) and the flightless dodo (above) of Mauritius has been overhunting by mankind.

they posed, so were easily approached and killed. Indeed, the notion that indigenous peoples in regions such as the Americas and Australasia lived in harmony and balance with their environment is proving to be utterly fallacious.

Extinctions of megafauna did not end there. A second wave of extinction began from the 1500s onwards, with the spread of sailors and new colonists from European countries. The Pacific region was especially vulnerable, where the fauna – particularly tortoises and birds – of many ocean islands were decimated. The demise of the dodo is iconic of this, but mankind was not the only culprit. Wherever rats, mice, pigs and other alien species were introduced, these animals wrought havoc on smaller species that humans did not regard as prey. In the oceans, and particularly the Southern Ocean, humans overexploited whales and seals from the late 1800s onwards, bringing several species of whale to the brink of extinction by the mid 1960s. Moreover, rampant overfishing during the last 50 years has virtually destroyed the once vast schools of fish that populated many oceanic regions, such as over the Grand Banks of Newfoundland, and many of the world's once productive fisheries have collapsed.

Most of the megafauna that existed 100 000 years ago are now gone. Africa was initially spared, however, probably because megafauna evolved alongside humans and developed a healthy respect for the dangers they posed. Unfortunately, the introduction of the rifle into Africa has brought rhinoceros and several antelope species to the brink of extinction. The bison of North America suffered

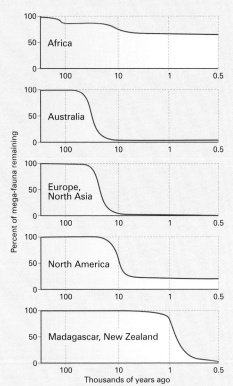

PROGRESSION OF THE SIXTH EXTINCTION

Following human migration and overhunting, the so-called Sixth Extinction has spread like a wave around the world, claiming mainly larger animals.

the same fate, where an estimated 30 million animals prior to European settlement were reduced to just 600 animals by 1900. The once ubiquitous passenger pigeon of North America was not so lucky. The last wild bird was shot in 1900 and the species finally became extinct in 1914 when the last individual died in captivity.

Sadly, the destruction is far from over. The advent and expansion of agriculture and forestry is proving to be very destructive as habitat is fragmented or destroyed. All species, irrespective of size and including plants and insects, are now vulnerable and are succumbing on a massive scale. Overall extinction rates are now about 10 000 times faster than normal and 50% of species we know today could be extinct by 2050. At its current rate, this will rank amongst the big five mass extinction events by the end of this century, and will certainly warrant description as the Sixth Extinction.

Gallo Images / Getty Images

WHAT IS MANKIND'S IMPACT ON EARTH?

Will great cities such as New York be preserved in the geological record if humanity becomes extinct?

The geological record of Earth is scattered with 'great events'. These include the Hadean Period's Heavy Bombardment of Earth by massive meteorites, the first appearance of life, the appearance of free oxygen in the atmosphere, and extinction of the dinosaurs. One clear message emerging from the fossil record is that *all species become extinct*. So it follows that humans will probably also become extinct in the future. If so, fossilized human bones will undoubtedly be preserved in sedimentary deposits, such as on the Gangetic plains, or on the Brahmaputra Delta, as well as in associated marine deposits. But what imprint will we leave in the geological record, other than just our bones, to show that we were remarkable?

One might imagine that the spectacular Aswan or Hoover dams, or large cities such as New York or Tokyo will all outlast us, but in reality, none will survive into the geological record. All will eventually be lost by erosion. The best chance for preserving a city would be burial under volcanic or sedimentary deposits, such as occurred at Pompeii. But in reality, most man-made constructions are no more durable than the rocks around us. Like rocks, our buildings will erode and almost none will survive into the distant future. After all, during the last 40 million years of the Cretaceous Period, about 2 to 3 km of rock were eroded off most of southern Africa. No man-made structures could survive such an onslaught.

What about other impacts? Since the 1750s, humans have dramatically increased the atmospheric concentration of carbon dioxide. How this trend will develop in the future is unclear, and although it will probably be recorded in the geological record, the increase will probably not last indefinitely. This is because the Earth's atmosphere is constantly being recycled, so that any short-term damage wrought by humans will eventually be corrected once we are gone, and a natural equilibrium will be restored.

Although our engineering feats will not survive, we will leave a lasting footprint – on life. Humans have had a profound effect on the biology of the planet. We have been responsible for the extinction of many animals across the globe, leaving a permanent record of our presence. However, this extinction has taken just a few tens of thousand of years, an interval generally too short to be resolved in the geological record. To future intelligent beings, this and other extinctions will appear as a simultaneous mass extinction, for which we are unlikely to be identified as the culprit, although our fossilized bones will be uniquely associated with it.

The Anthropocene age of humans has also been characterized by the spread of many species far beyond their natural ranges. In South Africa, invasive alien plant species include wattle, syringa, jacaranda and eucalyptus trees as well as dozens more. This is a worldwide phenomenon, and it is not restricted to plants alone. Our rivers are being invaded by alien fish species on a global scale, while marine organisms are spreading in the ballast of oil tankers, resulting in widespread alien marine invasions.

We therefore live in an age of increasing species extinction, but also one of biogeographic turmoil, and both phenomena will be preserved in the fossil record. Extinction terminates an evolutionary line,

Right: The mammoth was hunted to extinction towards the end of the last ice age; a casualty of man's spread around the globe.

Far right: Rivers can carve their way through the hardest rock, such as the granites that flank Augrabies Falls near Upington, and will ultimately destroy all traces of the world's great dams.

Terence McCarthy

Terence McCarthy

so that potential future diversity flowing from that species is lost forever. And while alien species may lead to the extinction of indigenous species, it also opens up evolutionary possibilities for new species in the future. Humans have commandeered much of the planet's resources, including the most useful land for agriculture, so when we go, we will leave a relative vacuum. Vacant niches and the new mix of species we have fostered will lead to a new explosion in biodiversity.

We may even have a more profound impact on life through genetic engineering of organisms considered useful to us. Where this will lead is unclear at present, because this science is still in its relative infancy. However, because the process is independent of sexually transmitted genes, genetic engineering could in principle result in novel organisms, or at least completely novel strains. If so, this would open up completely new evolutionary possibilities that might have no immediately obvious evolutionary roots.

So, our physical creations will almost certainly not withstand the onslaught of weathering and erosion over geological time, and will vanish after we are gone. However, our impact on Earth's flora and fauna will leave an indelible mark on the history and future of life in a post-*Homo sapiens* world. In this sense, mankind's effect on the environment has and will be profound, and certainly compares with great geological events.

Humanity has been responsible for spreading many organisms far beyond their natural ranges, such as the introduction of alien tree species into southern Africa for commercial forestry.

Terence McCarthy

WHAT IS THE IMPORTANCE OF THE KAROO FOSSILS?

Fossils are normally preserved in marine sedimentary rocks, which is the ultimate dumping place for material eroded from the land. Marine fossils are therefore very common. Rather special conditions are needed, however, to preserve sedimentary rocks deposited under terrestrial conditions. The area must be subsiding, creating space to accommodate the sediment, and, moreover, conditions must be such that the accumulated sediment is protected from erosion. Just such conditions existed in the Karoo from about 300 to 182 million years ago.

Some 300 million years ago, southern Africa emerged from beneath an ice cap several kilometres thick (see page 108). At that time, the Cape Fold Mountains we know today were more impressive, and probably like the modern Andes, complete with huge volcanoes. To the south lay a vast ocean, Panthalassa, and to the north of the range was the inland Karoo Sea, which was probably linked to Panthalassa, perhaps in a way similar to the Gibraltar Straits that link the Mediterranean Sea with the Atlantic Ocean. The northern shore of the Karoo Sea probably lay in the vicinity of the Witwatersrand, where it was shallow but became deeper in the south. Rivers rising in the north that emptied into the northern Karoo Sea formed huge deltas on which swamp forests

thrived, laying down vast coal deposits. Deltas on the southern shore were much smaller because of the rapidly deepening water, but these southerly rivers carried prodigious amounts of sediment into the Karoo Sea from erosion of the Cape Fold Mountains to the south.

Over time, the Karoo Sea progressively shrank as it filled with sediment, and the ocean gave way to extensive flood plains traversed by large rivers that were fed by snow melt from the mountain range to the south. Subsidence continued, however, allowing layer upon layer of flood plain sediment to accumulate. Conditions gradually became drier too, and what remained of the Karoo Sea evaporated into a series of salt pans that finally became an extensive sand desert as aridity increased. Then sediment accumulation was suddenly terminated by the eruption of vast quantities of lava 182 million years ago, which completely buried the desert under more than a kilometre of igneous rock.

Over most of the 120 million-year-period of sediment accumulation in the Karoo, conditions were terrestrial, with abundant swampy flood-plain environments. The muddy and shallow waters were ideal conditions for the fossilization of animals that died there. As a result, Karoo rocks contain abundant terrestrial and aquatic animal

FROM REPTILE TO MAMMAL – CHANGES IN THE BONES OF THE PALATE

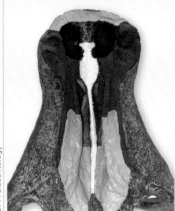
Theriognathus

Procynosuchus

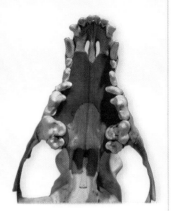
Dog

The Karoo strata were deposited when mammals began to diverge from reptiles, and its fossils reveal the successive anatomical changes that led to the gradual evolution of mammals. Important changes were the formation of a bony palate by the expansion of the maxilla (red) and palatine (pink) bones (above), and the development of a single jaw bone (opposite).

fossils from that time. It is fortunate that today's climate over much of the Karoo is arid, so that soils are thin and rock exposures abound. These conditions are ideal for fossil hunters, since fossils become exposed by erosion and are more easily found than under wetter climatic conditions, where soils tend to be thick and rock outcrops rare.

Karoo fossils represent a good sample of terrestrial and aquatic life forms over a 120 million-year-period. Quite fortuitously too, this particular time was a critical period in evolution because this was when the evolution of mammals from reptiles took place. Fossils from successively younger sediment layers therefore reveal the sequence of anatomical changes that led from reptiles to mammals. Especially important were the development of a bony palate and a reduction in the number of bones in the lower jaw, some of which were co-opted into the ear to form the hammer and anvil bones. Animals possessing these intermediate characteristics are known as therapsids or mammal-like reptiles, which dominated the animal world until the Permian mass extinction (248 million years ago) greatly reduced their diversity. Deposition of Karoo rocks also coincided with the origin of the dinosaurs, which began to dominate after the Permian mass extinction.

FROM REPTILE TO MAMMAL – CHANGES IN THE BONES OF THE JAW

Dimetrodon

Diademodon

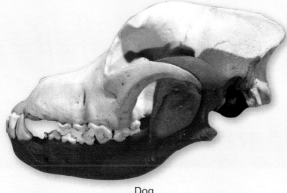

Dog

Karoo fossils therefore provide a complete record of the origin of mammals from their reptilian ancestors to the first true mammal, a small shrew-like animal that was found near the top of the Karoo strata in Lesotho. This fossil record has made the Karoo famous in palaeontological circles, because nowhere else in the world is the record from this time period so complete. The origin of dinosaurs is also preserved in Karoo fossils, although these have been less well studied than the therapsids. But that is now changing, and it is probable that the Karoo will yield important new insights into the early dinosaur lineage. In addition, the Karoo is proving to be an ideal place to investigate the cause and effects of the mass extinction event on terrestrial environments at the end of Permian Period. From a palaeontological perspective, the Karoo is therefore exceptionally important.

BPI Palaeontology

WHY ARE FOSSILIZED SEA SHELLS SOMETIMES FOUND ON MOUNTAIN TOPS?

Mountains form in a variety of ways (see page 36). The really high mountains of the world, like the Alps and the Himalayan range, formed by the collision of continents; Africa and Europe in the case of the Alps, and Asia and India in the case of the Himalaya (see page 38). Such collisions are a consequence of the constant movement of the Earth's continents. The collisions that formed the Alps and Himalaya involved the destruction of the Tethys Sea that once separated the land masses involved. Sediments that lay on the floor of this sea became compressed and folded, and then incorporated into the mountain range along the collision zone. It is for this reason that many of the high peaks in both the Alps and the Himalayan range (including Everest) are formed of sedimentary rocks, some of which contain fossilized marine organisms.

Many of these fossilized marine organisms were ancient molluscs with shells, just as their modern counterparts have. Their calcium carbonate (calcite) shells, as well as the external calcium carbonate plates, or liths, of minute oceanic phytoplankton, called coccolithophores, sometimes formed dense layers in the ancient sediments of shallow seas after they died and

HOW OCEAN FLOORS BECOME MOUNTAIN PEAKS

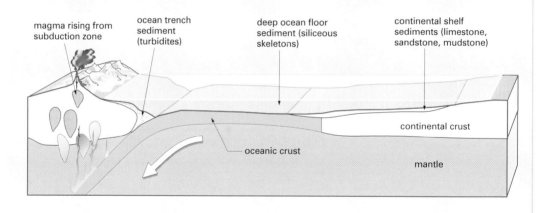

magma rising from subduction zone

ocean trench sediment (turbidites)

deep ocean floor sediment (siliceous skeletons)

continental shelf sediments (limestone, sandstone, mudstone)

continental crust

oceanic crust

mantle

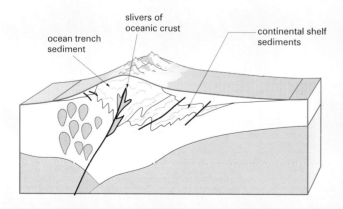

slivers of oceanic crust

ocean trench sediment

continental shelf sediments

The process of plate tectonics sometimes results in the closure of an ocean and the collision of its flanking continents. As the ocean closes, sedimentary deposits on the ocean floor are compressed and folded to form high mountains, such as the Alps and the Himalaya, thus including fossilized marine organisms in such mountains.

Cape Mountain rocks were originally deposited in a shallow sea, and were compressed as this sea closed. One of the most common species of marine animals living at that time were the trilobites, and localities such as Gydo Pass near Ceres in the Western Cape are well known for their trilobite fossils.

sank to the bottom. When these sediments were compressed, they formed limestone, which consists primarily of calcite. The white cliffs of Dover were formed in exactly this way, as were the limestone deposits also found in the high Alps.

Just as sedimentary layers were incorporated into the Alps and Himalaya, a similar process folded the sedimentary rocks that today form the mountains of the southern Cape (see page 102). For this reason, fossils of marine organisms such as trilobites and starfish are sometimes found in these rocks. Trilobites are ancient marine arthropods (meaning jointed legs) that flourished in the oceans of the Cambrian and Ordovician periods, which began about 540 million years ago, and lasted through to the Permian Period 280 million years ago. These organisms were extremely successful bottom-dwellers, and mostly just a few centimetres long. Because they had a hard chitinous exoskeleton, they were well preserved in the fossil record, which accounts for their relative abundance in the southern Cape mountains.

A trilobite, an ancient marine arthropod.

GLOSSARY

Abyssal plain Flat areas of the ocean floor.

Acheulian period A division of the Stone Age, extending approximately from 1.65 million to 200 000 years ago.

Agate Very fine-grained quartz, usually showing concentric colour banding. Formed in cavities in rock (often gas bubbles trapped in lava).

Agulhas Sea An inland sea that covered what is now the southern Cape between about 500 million and 330 million years ago.

Albedo A material's ability to reflect heat and light.

Alluvial plain Broad, flat region formed by coalesced river flood plains.

Ammonite Extinct diverse group of floating or swimming marine molluscs with coiled, chambered shells.

Andesite Fine-grained igneous rock (volcanic) consisting mainly of amphibole (calcium, aluminium, iron and magnesium silicate) and plagioclase.

Anorthosite A rock composed mainly of plagioclase.

Anthropocene Name proposed for the time period when human activities began to influence the planet significantly, generally assumed to commence in the mid-nineteenth century.

Aquifer A porous zone below the Earth's surface that holds water.

Archaea, Archaebacteria A primitive form of bacteria.

Arthropod A member of the great group of invertebrate animals, which includes crustaceans, arachnids and insects, all characterized by having an external skeleton made of a hard substance called chitin, and a variable number of jointed legs.

Asteroid Small bodies (<1 000 km diameter) orbiting the Sun between Mars and Jupiter.

Asthenosphere Zone within the Earth between depths of about 70 and 200 km possessing relatively lower seismic velocities, probably due to its very plastic nature. Also referred to as the Low Velocity Zone (or Layer) or LVZ.

Banded iron formation A sedimentary rock consisting of alternating bands of fine, white quartz (silicon dioxide) and black and red oxides of iron.

Barycentre Common centre of mass of mutually orbiting bodies.

Basalt Fine-grained igneous rock (volcanic) consisting of plagioclase and pyroxene.

Basement Rocks, usually granite or related rocks, that lie beneath the oldest layered rocks (usually sedimentary) in a region.

Basin A local depression in the Earth's surface.

Batholith A large body (>100 km^2) of intrusive igneous rock.

Biosphere The thin envelope around the Earth, at or near its surface, in which life can exist.

Breccia A rock consisting of angular fragments set in a matrix of finer material.

Calcite A mineral consisting of calcium carbonate.

Cambrian Explosion Name given to the sudden appearance of fossilized body parts of marine organisms 545 million years ago.

Chert A sedimentary rock consisting of very fine-grained quartz (silicon dioxide) formed by chemical precipitation from water.

Chloroplast A structure inside a cell in which photosynthesis takes place.

Clathrates Compounds formed of loosely bound water and gases such as methane.

Comet A large body consisting mainly of ice laced with dust that orbits the Sun in a very eccentric orbit.

Conglomerate A coarse-grained sedimentary rock consisting of pebbles, cobbles or boulders with sandy material filling the spaces between larger particles.

Continental crust The Earth's crust beneath continents. It consists mainly of granite and related rocks and is usually about 35 km thick.

Continental drift The theory that continents move relative to each other.

Continental shelf The fringes of continents that are submerged below sea level.

Core The innermost portion of the Earth, believed to consist of nickel and iron.

Cosmic radiation High energy nuclear particles that enter the Solar System from deep space.

Cratons The stable, ancient cores of continents. They are usually made up of granodiorites and greenstone belts.

Crust The outermost layer of the Earth situated above the Mohorovičić discontinuity.

Cyanobacteria A group of microorganisms capable of oxygen-producing photosynthesis.

Dolerite A medium-grained igneous rock consisting of plagioclase and pyroxene; occurs as dykes or sills.

Doline Area of slowly subsiding ground caused by subsurface erosion.

Dolomite A mineral, calcium magnesium carbonate, or a rock consisting entirely of grains of this mineral.

Dome An uplift that is more or less circular in plan, with rock layers dipping away from its centre.

Donga Gulley formed by soil erosion.

Dwyka Group Rock formation in southern Africa deposited by glacial activity about 300 million years ago.

Dyke A tabular intrusive rock that cuts across other rocks.

Eubacteria A primitive form of bacteria.

Fault A surface along which a rock mass has been broken and displaced.

Fault scarp A step in the Earth's surface caused by vertical displacement of a rock mass along a fault.

Feldspar A group of minerals consisting of sodium, calcium and potassium aluminium silicates.

Flood basalt Extensive eruption of basalt lava in which hundreds of thousands to millions of cubic kilometres of lava are erupted in a geologically short period (around 1 million years or less).

Flowstone Curtain-like rock formation lining the wall of a cave; may also occur as a coating on the floor of a cave.

Fold A bend in a layer of rock.

Foraminifera Small marine organisms that usually have calcareous shells with minute holes (belong to a subdivision of the Protozoa).

Fracture zone A linear zone along which many faults are developed; the zone of fracture extending from a transform fault across the ocean floor.

Gaining stream A river that obtains some of its water from the inflow of ground water.

Geothermal gradient The rate of increase in rock temperature with increasing depth in the Earth, usually expressed in °C per km depth.

Glacial striations Grooves and scratches on a rock surface formed by glaciers dragging rock fragments over the surface.

Glacial pavement A rock surface that has been smoothed and grooved by glaciers.

Gneiss A coarse-grained metamorphic rock having a distinct banding of lighter and darker layers; its mineral composition is usually similar to granite.

Gondwana The ancient continental landmass made up of the present landmasses of Africa, South America, the Falkland Isles, India, Australia, New Zealand, Antarctica and Madagascar that is believed to have formed about 500 million years ago.

Graben An elongated block of rock that has been lowered by faulting relative to the surrounding blocks.

Graded river profile The smooth curve formed by plotting a graph of the elevation of the bed of a river with increasing distance from its mouth.

Granite A coarse-grained igneous rock consisting mainly of quartz (silicon dioxide) and alkali feldspar (sodium and potassium aluminium silicates).

Group A term used in stratigraphy to denote a related group of layered rocks.

Gutenberg discontinuity The sudden change in seismic velocity that occurs at the boundary between the Earth's mantle and core.

Gymnosperm A seed plant with seeds not enclosed in an ovary; includes conifers, cycads, cycadeoids and ginkgos.

Hadean Era The geological period forming the earliest part of the Archaean Eon, including the final stages of formation of Earth by meteorite bombardment (4 600 million to 3 800 million years ago).

Holocene The geological period that began approximately 10 000 years ago.

Hominin The group of primates that includes all the bipedal forms as well as humans i.e. all the fossil genera such as *Australopithecus, Ardipithecus, Kenyanthropus* and *Homo.*

Hotspot The expression at the Earth's surface of a mantle plume, usually taking the form of localized, intense volcanic activity.

Hydrothermal fluid Hot ground water containing various dissolved substances.

Hydrothermal vent The point of discharge of hydrothermal fluid, usually on the sea floor.

Hypersaline Water that is saturated in salt.

Ice Age A prolonged period of lower temperature on Earth during which ice caps greatly expand.

Interglacial period Relatively warm period separating Ice Ages.

Iron formation Sedimentary rock consisting mainly of iron oxide minerals.

Island arc An arc of volcanic islands (e.g. Japanese archipelago, Aleutian Islands) formed where one plate containing oceanic crust is subducted beneath another.

Joint A fracture in a rock mass along which no significant relative movement has taken place.

Kaapvaal Craton The ancient core of the southern African continent, formed between 3 600 million and 3 100 million years ago. It consists mainly of granodiorite batholiths and greenstone belts.

Karoo Sea An inland sea that existed across southern Africa between 300 and about 250 million years ago.

Kibaran Belt Linear zones of metamorphic rocks on the African continent formed about 1 200 to 1 000 million years ago.

Kimberlite A rare igneous rock consisting of silicate minerals rich in magnesium, iron and alkali metals; it is the source rock of diamonds.

Late Bombardment A period about 3 900 million years ago when the Moon and probably all of the inner planets were subjected to bombardment by large meteorites and comets.

Laurasia Ancient continental landmass consisting of Europe, North America, Asia and Greenland.

Layered intrusion An igneous intrusion that is composed of layers of rock of different mineralogical composition.

Lithification The process by which loose sediment is converted into sedimentary rock.

Lithosphere The relatively rigid outer layer of the Earth, including the crust and the upper part of the mantle.

Little Ice Age An unusually cold period between about 1315 and 1860.

Magma Molten rock before it erupts on the surface.

Magma chamber A large space below the Earth's surface occupied by molten rock.

Magnetic declination Deviation of magnetic north from the geographic North Pole.

Magnetic inclination The angle that a compass needle will form relative to the horizontal: it is zero at the equator and 90° at the poles.

Mammal-like reptile The common name used for the group of primitive tetrapods that are the distant ancestors of mammals.

Mantle Region of the Earth's interior between the base of the crust and the core.

Mantle plume A hot, buoyant mass of material that rises from deep within the Earth to the base of the lithosphere.

Matrix The relatively finer-grained material occupying the spaces between larger particles in a rock.

Mesosphere Zone of the Earth's mantle below the asthenosphere.

Metamorphic belt A linear zone on the Earth's crust underlain by metamorphic rocks.

Metamorphic rock A rock formed from pre-existing rocks that have been subjected to elevated temperature and pressure (and usually involving hot fluids) such that their mineral composition has undergone change.

Metamorphism Alteration of the mineral composition of a rock brought about by exposure to elevated temperature and pressure (and possibly hot fluids).

Meteorite A particle of natural material that has fallen to Earth from space.

Micro-fossil Remains of tiny plants or animals that require the use of a microscope to be studied; includes fossil bacteria, algae, pollens, spores, protozoans, microscopic crustaceans, etc.

Mid-ocean ridge A mountain range on the sea floor where tectonic plates separate.

Mineral A naturally occurring chemical compound.

Mitochondria Bodies within a cell where a chemical that transfers energy within the cell is formed.

Mobile belt A term often used synonymously with Metamorphic belt.

Moho/Mohorovičić discontinuity Shallowest major seismic discontinuity below the Earth's surface, which marks the base of the Earth's crust; it arises from the difference in chemical composition between the crust and the mantle.

Mountain belt A long mountain chain (e.g. Andes).

Nebula A mass of dust and gas in space.

Nuclear fusion The process of fusion of nuclear particles or atomic nuclei to form heavier atomic nuclei.

Oceanic crust The crust that underlies the oceans (excluding continental shelves).

Palaeoclimate Climate in a past time.

Palaeomagnetism Magnetism that has become imprinted in rocks when they formed.

Pangaea A supercontinent consisting of all of the Earth's present continents. It is believed to have formed about 300 million years ago.

Panthalassa The great ocean that counterpoised the supercontinent Pangaea.

Pediment A gently sloping erosion surface at the base of a mountain.

Phanerozoic Eon The period of Earth history extending from 545 million years ago to the present.

Photosphere The outer, incandescent surface of a star.

Photosynthesis A metabolic process in which light or heat energy is used to convert carbon dioxide and water to carbohydrate.

Pillow lava Pillow-shaped masses of lava formed during undersea volcanic eruptions, or when erupting lava issues into a lake or other body of water.

Plagioclase A mineral consisting of sodium and calcium aluminium silicate.

Planetesimals Small bodies that grow into planets by a process of accretion.

Plate boundary A region where the rigid plates that form the outer layer of the Earth come into contact. At these boundaries plates may converge, diverge or slide past each other.

Plate tectonics The theory proposing that the outer layer of the Earth (lithosphere) consists of separate, rigid plates (in which the continents are embedded) that move relative to each other and in the process move the continents.

Pluton A body (<100 km^2) of intrusive igneous rock.

Positron A positively charged electron.

Procaryote A life form consisting of simple, single cells, such as cyanobacteria, that are not specialized and do not have organelles or a nucleus inside them.

Proterozoic Era The period of Earth history extending from 2 500 million to 545 million years ago.

Pumice A frothy, natural glass

Pyroclastic flow An avalanche of hot, often incandescent, volcanic rock and dust, together with superheated gases, emanating from a volcano.

Pyroxene An iron magnesium silicate; calcium-bearing and calcium-free varieties exist.

Quartzite A sedimentary rock consisting of sand grains (composed of the mineral quartz) in which the grains interlock due to recrystallization (usually a result of heating), making the rock extremely hard.

Red bed A sandstone or siltstone with a red colour, caused by the presence of red oxides of iron.

Reef 1. A structure built by marine organisms.
2. A planar body of rock that is enriched in a mineral of economic importance (e.g. gold).

Rhyolite A fine-grained igneous rock (volcanic) consisting mainly of quartz (silicon dioxide) and alkali feldspar (sodium and potassium aluminium silicates).

Rift valley A valley of regional extent formed by the collapse of a fault-bounded central zone.

Ring of Fire The name given to the belt of volcanoes that surrounds the Pacific Ocean.

Ripple marks Small waves on a sand surface produced by flowing water or wind. These are often preserved in sedimentary rocks.

Seafloor spreading The theory that new ocean floor (oceanic crust) is being created at, and is spreading away from, mid-ocean ridges.

Seamount A conical mountain rising from the sea floor; they are probably submerged volcanoes.

Sedimentary rock A rock formed by the accumulation and consolidation of sediment.

Sedimentary structure A structure (e.g. ripple marks, cross bedding) that formed in sediment at the time of deposition; often preserved in the sediment after it has been converted to rock.

Seismic discontinuity An interface within the Earth at which the velocity of seismic waves suddenly changes.

Seismic wave A vibration within the Earth created by the release of energy either on or below the surface.

Shield volcano A large volcano shaped like a circular, medieval shield, constructed by repeated flows of fluid lava (usually basalt). The slopes seldom exceed 10°.

Silicate mineral A mineral in which silicon is a major constituent.

Sill A sheet-like body of igneous rock intruded between layers of older rock.

Smoker A hot spring on the sea floor where cooling of the spring water induces precipitation of dissolved solids, producing smoke-like clouds in the water.

Solar Wind The stream of nuclear particles (mainly protons and electrons) ejected from the Sun.

Spring mound A raised area around the mouth of a spring formed by precipitation of material from the spring water.

Stratovolcano A steep-sided volcano made up of layers of ash, volcanic rubble and lava flows.

Stratum (pl. strata) A layer of sedimentary rock.

Stromatolite A mound-like growth of carbonate rock, formed by the accumulation of calcium carbonate crystals on slimy algal or bacterial colonies.

Subduction Subsidence of the edge of a plate into the mantle.

Subgroup A term used in stratigraphy to denote a related group of layered rocks: subordinate to a Group.

Supercontinent A single continent formed by the amalgamation of several previously separate continental masses.

Supergroup A group of rock strata formed during a single, major and widespread episode of rock accumulation.

Supernova A tremendous stellar explosion involving the almost total destruction of a star.

Tethys Sea A sea that is believed to have once separated Gondwana and Laurasia, the closing of which gave rise to the Alps and the Himalayan mountains.

Tetrapod Vertebrate animals possessing four limbs instead of fins – i.e. amphibians, reptiles, mammals and birds.

Therapsid The diverse group of mammal-like reptiles from which mammals evolved.

Thermohaline circulation Ocean circulation driven by changes in water density due to variations in salinity and temperature.

Tidal flat A large, flat area of land that is inundated at high tide. Tidal flats are usually covered by mud, silt and sand.

Tidalite A sedimentary rock deposited under the influence of tides and in which layering due to tides can be discerned.

Tillite A rock made of unsorted, unstratified glacial material.

Transform faults Strike-slip (wrench) faults usually lying perpendicular to a mid-ocean ridge that compensate for different spreading rates along the length of the ridge.

Trench An elongated depression on the sea floor formed above a subducting plate.

Trilobite An early form of scuttling marine arthropod, distantly related to lobsters, crabs, etc.

Triple junction A point on Earth where three tectonic plates meet, commonly, but not always, formed by the intersection of three rift systems.

Tsunami A very large ocean wave caused by a major geological disturbance such as an earthquake, volcanic explosion or landslide. Often incorrectly referred to as a tidal wave.

Turbidite A sedimentary deposit formed by a turbidity current.

Turbidity current A sediment-rich slurry that cascades down the continental slope onto the abyssal plain below.

Ur Believed to be the Earth's oldest continent, consisting of cratonic areas of South Africa, Madagascar, India and Western Australia. It is believed to have formed between 3 000 million and 1 500 million years ago.

Vein (in geology) A small, dyke-like intrusive body.

Weathering Chemical decomposition of rocks as a result of exposure to the atmosphere.

INDEX

Illustrations, diagrams, graphs & tables are indicated by *italic* page numbers

Published by Struik Nature
  (an imprint of Random House Struik (Pty) Ltd)
Reg. No. 1966/003153/07
80 McKenzie Street, Cape Town, 8001
PO Box 1144, Cape Town, 8000, South Africa

Visit us at **www.randomstruik.co.za**

First published in 2009
10 9 8 7 6 5 4 3 2

Copyright © in text, 2009: Terence McCarthy
Copyright © in photographs, 2009: as individually credited
Copyright © in illustrations, 2009: Random House Struik
  (Pty) Ltd / Terence McCarthy / Exxaro

Publisher: Pippa Parker
Managing editor: Helen de Villiers
Editor: Mike Lucas
Project manager: Colette Alves
Design director: Janice Evans
Designer: Louise Topping
Illustrator: Colin Bleach
Proofreader: Cynthia Kemp
Indexer: Cora Ovens
Picture researcher: Colette Stott

Reproduction by Hirt & Carter Cape (Pty) Ltd
Printed and bound by CTP Book Printers
ISO 12647 compliant

ISBN 978 1 77007 485 9

Also available in Afrikaans as
Hoe op Aarde?
ISBN 978 1 77007 480 4

Photographic credits: front cover: (main photograph) Walter Knirr / IOA; **(bottom left to right)** Bruce Cairncross; Greatstock! / Corbis; BPI Palaeontology; Danja Kohler / IOA; **back cover:** Lanz von Hörsten / IOA; **page 4 (top to bottom):** US Department of Energy / Science Photo Library; Fiona McIntosh / IOA; Ian Michler / IOA; Bruce Cairncross; **page 5 (top to bottom):** Gallo Images / Getty Images; Terence McCarthy; Fritz Wagener; David McCarthy; **page 6:** Hein von Hörsten / IOA; **page 26:** Lanz von Hörsten / IOA; **page 52:** Keith Young / IOA; **page 68:** Walter Knirr / IOA; **page 100:** Roger de la Harpe / IOA; **page 144:** Vanessa Burger